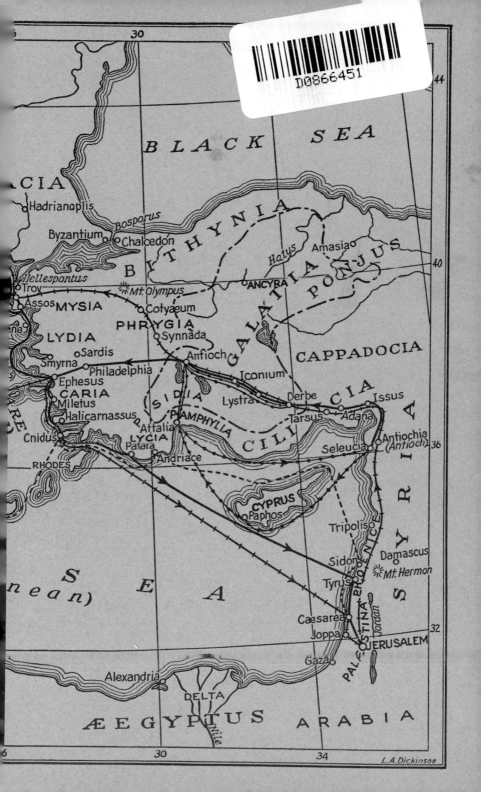

I, PAUL

Books by Rex Miller

_____

I, JOHN

I, PAUL

I, PAUL

An "Autobiography" of the
Apostle to the Gentiles

by

REX MILLER

DUELL, SLOAN AND PEARCE
NEW YORK

To My Mother

Preface

T. R. Glover whimsically remarks that "Luke and Paul are both careless or absent-minded about dates." From this arises the difficulty in establishing a completely satisfactory chronology of the career of the Apostle to the Gentiles.

There are two chief sources of information about Paul's life. One of them is his remarkable series of letters. The other is that portion of the Acts of the Apostles which relates Paul's adventures.

The conventional procedure with biographers has been to combine and synchronize as closely as possible these two sources. Difficulties, of course, arise. The two do not always fit together.

It has recently become the fashion to abandon this attempt at synthesis; to accept as basic only such portions of the letters as are judged authentic, and to discard anything that does not fit into this scheme.

For obvious reasons, I have been obliged to adopt the conventional procedure. The other method, of undoubted value in a critical sense, and in a work of scholarly research, is not at all adapted to the needs of an attempted "autobiography." It destroys more than it creates, and leaves the "autobiographer" well supplied with doubts and uncertainties, but ill equipped with the positive material he requires.

The vast literature on the subject of Paul presents hundreds of opinions, many of them in conflict. Yet certain important facts stand out, and the Apostle emerges from any analysis as an inspiring and powerful character. His significance for the Christian world is too great to be obscured by disagreements among scholars.

All the epistles attributed to Paul have here been accepted as genuine, except Hebrews; Ephesians is taken to be a Pauline letter, though not addressed originally to the Ephesians.

The apocryphal *Acts of Paul and Thekla* has not been ignored, but an effort has been made to reduce it to the realm of reasonableness, and to retain only such portions as seem plausible and in keeping with the known character and career of the Apostle.

For the period following the close of the narrative in Acts, the general sequence outlined by Conybeare and Howson, and by numerous other more recent authorities, has been accepted.

An attempt has been made, while writing the entire story in modern English, to retain something of the flavor of the King James version of the Bible. The various modern translations of the New Testament, notably Weymouth's, have been consulted, but no single text has been precisely followed.

This book is written by a layman, primarily for laymen. It seeks to provide an historical background which will make Paul's career more real, more interesting to students of the Bible. Points of theological and sectarian controversy have been avoided, as far as possible.

REX MILLER

I, PAUL

One

I HAVE fought a good fight, I have finished my course, I have kept the faith.

Henceforth there is laid up for me a crown of righteousness, which the Lord, the righteous judge, shall give me at that day: and not to me only, but to all them also that love his appearing.

For thirty years I have served the cause of Christ. Often have I been flogged, and many times imprisoned. Thousands of miles have I traveled by land and sea, bringing the glad tidings to both Jews and Gentiles.

From the plots of enemies, from earthquake and shipwreck, my God has saved me. Ever have I been conscious of His loving presence. He is nearer to me even than this Roman soldier whose arm is chained to mine, who sits beside me as I write, whose eye wanders curiously across the unfamiliar script that flows from my reed pen.

I am a prisoner, a prisoner in the cause of the Lord;

yet my spirit is free from bonds. I am held captive, here at Rome, but I am not in bondage.

My eyes cannot see beyond the limit of this rock-walled prison chamber; yet my vision reaches out to Ephesus, to Antioch, to Corinth, to Jerusalem, to a score of other towns and cities where I have planted or succored churches: to Philippi, to Tarsus, to Thessalonica, to Athens.

The Lord has kept me ever on the move; taken my feet and guided them, like leaves blown by a restless wind, across the surface of the earth. Seldom but when in bonds have I remained at rest.

Yet these present chains irk me no longer. My course is run. I am like a fleet-footed athlete I once saw at Corinth, at the Games, who, having made his last circuit of the stadium, and won his race, submitted to the embraces of his friends—such sweet bondage—and bowed his head to receive the chaplet of Isthmian pine which was his prize.

Whatever Nero's court may rule, I am the victor in this race of life. Mine is the joy of work well done. No sentence of Rome's praetor can stand against the verdict of that righteous judge to whom alone I do commit my cause.

*　　*　　*

I was that Saul who, three long decades since, stood by and saw poor Stephen stoned to death, consenting to the crime.

(How strange it seems to write, "I was that Saul." Was I indeed that Saul? How cruel a man he was!)

That Saul—that once was I—stood and smiled the cold, embittered smile that once was mine, as through the city gate rushed out an angry mob of screaming, snarling Jews with Stephen in their midst, like jackals with a disputed bit of carrion.

They were not surprised to find me there. Had I not by artful questions in the synagogue led Stephen to condemn himself before them? I would not soil my hands—my proud Pharisaic hands—upon him, but I knew well where they would bring him.

There stood I, aloof from murder, yet the doer of it. They threw off their outer garments and left them in my care, that they might with freer movements batter his poor frame with flinty roadside stones.

"Lord Jesus, receive my spirit!" arose his voice above the shrieks of rage; his clear, strong voice that but an hour before, or less, had rung so boldly through the synagogue.

Between the wide-spread legs of a sturdy smith who held a rock poised high above his head, I saw poor Stephen on his knees.

"Lord, lay not this sin to their charge," he prayed aloud, so that even I could hear him. And when he had said this, he fell asleep.

God grant that when my time arrives to bend beneath a Roman sword at some wayside spot beyond this wicked city's walls, I may be such a man as Stephen was, outside Jerusalem.

*   *   *

That Saul, who murdered Stephen and harried the sect of the Nazarenes, was I.

From boyhood, for a score of years, I had trained myself to but a single end: to be a vigilant guardian of our Jewish faith. I was a Hebrew of the Hebrews, of the stock of Israel, of the tribe of Benjamin, circumcised the eighth day, blameless before the Hebrew law, a Pharisee.

To be a Jew in Tarsus, where I was born, was not easy. Ours was a Greek city in a Roman province. Both the prevailing language and the civic rule were alien to my people. The ruder folk spoke dialects of Asia, but the literature and the government were European: Greek and Roman.

We Jews lived in this pagan atmosphere, but we were not of it. We could speak Greek; my father had gained the precious right of Roman citizenship, which I inherited. But we were Jews. We mingled with these pagans in the marts of trade, but at home we were neither Greeks nor Romans; we were Hebrews.

We were a little Jewish island in a sea of pagans. My youth was spent in two separate worlds. At home, I learned the law and the prophets; I went on Sabbaths to the synagogue. But in the bazaar where I worked, apprenticed to the tent-maker's craft, the stream of commerce that flowed around me bore on its surface a mingled crowd of Arabs, Egyptians, Phoenicians, Cypriots, Greeks and Romans, a polyglot horde.

The talk in the bazaar, except among my fellow apprentices and some traders who were Jews, was of the games, the races in the stadium, the comedies in the theater; all punctuated with oaths upon the names of heathen deities.

As I sat cross-legged, sewing at my tents, or stretched the coarse haircloth upon the frames for cutting, I heard the gossip of all the Eastern lands, with now and again a scrap of pagan philosophy that filtered down into our humble market-street from the gardens on the hillside, where our famous Stoic scholars were wont to stroll and spin their philosophic webs.

All this Greek chatter, all this Godless talk, only served to turn me more eagerly to the faith of my fathers, to make me a more ardent Jew. I could not but scoff at the frivolous lives and manners of the unthinking throngs who peopled the trading quarters of our city, along the wharves and streets beside the River Cnidus, where Tarsus' shipping lay in port.

Yet I know now that this experience of my youth was but a preparation for a life work yet to come, a work that has taken me, much of the time, among the Gentiles. Had I not learned their ways, formed friends among them, heard their talk, listened to their reasoning, I should not have been so fit to carry among them the true, the living Word of God.

*   *   *

One does not spend boyhood days in markets where the merchants of all nations congregate, one does not live as a youth in a thriving seaport, without getting a thirst for travel.

Many a seaman's tale, many a camel-driver's legend, I listened to as I worked at my craft in Tarsus. I longed to visit distant lands. I desired the adventure of long journeys. I plied every visiting trader that came into the shop with questions about the places he had visited.

The things I learned from these wanderers have stood me in good stead, for much of my life has been spent in journeying, and few have been the places I had gained no knowledge of, before I visited them.

God, although I knew it not, was making me ready for His service.

*   *   *

First of the journeys that I made was at the age of thirteen, to Jerusalem. Most Hebrew lads of devout families made this pilgrimage at about this age, but with few of them did it mark such a turning-point in life as with me.

Here at the heart of Israel I found all the things my soul had craved. Here was indeed Zion. Here beat the pulse of Jewish being.

With what pride did my father, in presenting me in the temple, declare that I fully understood the Hebrew law, and was ready to fulfill my duties as a Jew, and take full responsibility for my sins!

The learned doctors were pleased with my answers to

their questions, and marked me as a youth of promise. From that moment I gave myself without stint to serve the Hebrew cause, and strove to perfect myself in all the learning of our people.

I was accepted as a pupil of the great Gamaliel, most famous teacher of those times. At his feet, in his school at Jerusalem, I sat with other lads who were chosen from all Jewry, and learned the most sacred tenets of our faith.

The Hebrew law became within me a brightly burning flame, that warmed me to combat with zeal the enemies of our religion, and win over the skeptics.

Here is a prayer that Gamaliel taught us:

"Let there be no hope to them who forsake the true religion; and let heretics, how many soever they be, all perish as in a moment. And let the kingdom of pride be speedily rooted out and broken in our days."

We prayed this prayer because we saw Judaism threatened with apostasy and heresy. Some of our people were being lured into heathen ways of life, and others were joining sects which threatened the sacred unity of Israel.

Most dangerous among these sects, or so it seemed to us, was that of the Nazarenes. (How strange it seems to use that old, discarded term for those who now are known as Christians!)

These Nazarenes were followers of Jesus of Nazareth, whom they claimed to be the Messiah, come to lead Israel out of bondage. It seemed to matter not with them that this Jesus had been tried before our supreme council, the Sanhedrin, and also before Pontius Pilate, and had been convicted, and sentenced to shameful death upon a cross. They declared that he had arisen from the tomb and been seen by great numbers of their sect, thus proving himself the Son of God, and worthy of their worship and devotion.

As I rose higher in the counsels of the priests and Pharisees, I found them deeply concerned with this sect's rapid growth. The Jewish leaders had disposed of Jesus—or so they thought—but his followers continued to present a serious problem.

The plot the high priests had hatched against the carpenter from Nazareth had been carried out to perfection. Every step of it had proceeded according to schedule: the seizure of the culprit outside the city at midnight, when no admiring throngs could aid him; the hasty trial before daybreak before the Sanhedrin, assembled for the purpose; the speedy winning over of the unwilling Pilate by threatening to report to Rome that he was lenient to one who claimed to rule where only Caesar's writ should run; the swift crucifixion between two thieves; the prompt removal of the culprit's body from the cross before the feast of the Passover. There had been hardly a hitch in the proceedings.

Yet all this plotting seemed to have been in vain. The story of Jesus' resurrection took such hold upon the thoughts of his disciples that they forgot his trial, his conviction, his ignominious death—forgot everything but the glorious fact of his rising from the tomb.

They began to make converts even in the most unexpected places. Two distant kinsmen of mine, Andronicus and Junias, went over to them. Something had to be done.

I had by this time grown to be one of the most prominent young Jews of Jerusalem, on terms of intimacy with the high priests and the Sanhedrin. They took me into their confidence. I was still young and, being unmarried and childless, could not be a member of the great council. Yet my voice carried more weight with them than some of the members. They made me a special agent to spy upon and persecute the Nazarenes.

* * *

One of the most active among their preachers, and the most outspoken, was Stephen. His speaking won them many converts. As one of seven deacons who looked after the business affairs of the sect, he enjoyed great authority among them. We decided to do away with him.

He, like other Nazarenes, made a practice of speaking in the synagogues of Jerusalem, being invited to do so by prominent members of the congregations. One synagogue which he frequented consisted largely of Jews and proselytes, or converts to Judaism, from countries other than Judea. Some of them, known to me, were from my native province of Cilicia, from the Roman province of Asia, from Alexandria, from Cyrene, and elsewhere. This was called the synagogue of the libertines, or freedmen, because it had originally been formed to accommodate enfranchised slaves and their descendants.

I easily prevailed upon my friends in this synagogue

to start an argument with Stephen when he came there. But Stephen spoke with such eloquence and skill that he soon routed his opponents.

Since we of the high priest's party were determined to get him out of the way, and we could not defeat him in debate, we had resort to treachery. There were always hangers-on who could be employed to do perjury, and we hired some of them. They worked under instructions from my force of secret police.

These hired perjurers accused Stephen of having spoken blasphemy against Moses and against God. Others of our agents stirred up the congregations of the synagogues against him, until they finally seized him and hurried him before the Sanhedrin to be tried.

Our agents appeared before the court as witnesses against Stephen, as it sat in the audience chamber adjoining the temple courtyard.

"This man," they declared, "continuously speaks blasphemous words against this holy place and against the law. We have heard him say that this Jesus of Nazareth whom he worships will destroy this place and change the sacred customs bequeathed to us by Moses."

"Are these things so?" asked the high priest, Caiaphas, who was presiding over the court.

Whereupon Stephen, without even deigning to answer the question, launched a counter-accusation against the court that was assembled to try him.

"O stiffnecked creatures," he cried, "you always resist the Holy Spirit, even as your forefathers did. Which of the prophets did not your forefathers persecute? They killed those who foretold the coming of that just man

whom you have now betrayed and murdered, Jesus the
Christ. You received the law through inspiration, but
you have not kept it!"

The learned judges were cut to the heart by what Stephen said, and gnashed their teeth at him in fury.

But he, full of the Holy Spirit, looked steadfastly up
to heaven.

"Behold," he said in ecstasy, "I see the heavens
opened and the Son of man standing at the right hand
of God."

Instantly there was tumult in the courtroom. Some
members of the court covered their ears with their hands
so that they might not hear such blasphemy. All of them
shouted aloud to drown the sound of Stephen's words.
Then they fell upon him like wolves, striking and beating him, tearing his garments.

Our secret agents joined in the assault. The mob closed
around him and he was hustled out of the audience
chamber, across the temple court, through the temple
gates, and out the nearest gate of the city.

I was there before them, and saw him stoned. Ah,
Stephen, brave Stephen, first of the Christian martyrs,
your blood was not shed in vain! I, who caused it to
flow upon the stony ground, have seen churches of the
living God spring up from the earth it nourished.

*   *   *

We did not stop with Stephen. The time was opportune for persecuting the Nazarenes, and we made the
most of it.

Pontius Pilate, the Roman procurator, or governor, of

Judea, had just been recalled to Rome to answer for his
misdeeds. It was he who had handed Jesus over to be
crucified. Yet it was not for this that he was censured
by the emperor, but for his tactlessness and cruelty to
the Jews. His recall to Rome to be punished for his
wrongs was celebrated as a Jewish victory.

With Pilate out of the way, we were able to take
the law into our own hands. We had no legal right, of
course, to kill Stephen; only the Roman rulers could,
except in a few special cases, impose the penalty of
death. But with Pilate gone, and his successor not yet
in office, we felt secure in dealing roughly with Stephen
and other Nazarenes.

Freed for the moment from the supervision of a
Roman governor, we took advantage of our opportunity.
I turned my agents loose upon the Nazarenes with re-
newed fury. I made havoc of their church, going myself
into the house of every member of the sect who could
be discovered, casting both men and women into prison
and seizing their property.

I had to warn my men not to kill many of these people; wholesale murder would have brought the wrath of
Rome upon us. But short of murder, I did what I could
to drive them out of Jerusalem, and I succeeded.

Soon, those who were not in prison had been fright-
ened into hiding, or scattered throughout Judea and Samaria.

My thoroughness pleased the Sanhedrin, and especially the high priest, Caiaphas. I was always welcome
in his house. He fanned my zeal into brighter flame, and

I decided to carry my persecutions beyond Jerusalem, into any fields, however distant, where the hated sect had taken root.

From Damascus came reports that certain of their members, driven from Jerusalem, had appeared in the synagogues there, preaching and making new converts. I determined to pursue them into the Syrian city, and obtained letters from Caiaphas giving me authority, if I could find any of the Nazarenes, either men or women, to take them prisoners and bring them bound to Jerusalem.

Proudly I set off on my new exploit. I was already in high favor with the rulers of our people; if I could carry off this new adventure with success, what might it not mean for my future, my career in the service of my people?

I was no Sadducee, as the high priests were, and I was not of the little caste that made the high priesthood almost a monopoly in the hands of a single family. But I was an ardent Jew, a young man with a record of achievement. And Caiaphas had a daughter.

Two

IF YOU approach Damascus by the Jerusalem road, you will reach a point, not far outside the city wall, where desert suddenly gives way to garden.

Along this road I passed, one bright midday in early spring, just thirty years ago. The members of our little caravan, sensing the approaching end of the tedious six-day journey from Jerusalem, were in high spirits. The sun beat hotly upon our shoulders, and from the padding hoofs of the camels clouds of fine dust arose and all but smothered us. We could see ahead the fresh greenness of the well-watered plain, and the gleaming whiteness of the city's houses scattered among their groves and gardens.

I was elated at the prospect of activity within the famous, ancient, beautiful city that lay ahead. These Nazarenes should learn that, even in the distant seclusion of a pagan city, no Jew could elude the watchful-

ness of the temple authorities at Jerusalem! Our Sanhedrin sat in the temple compound, but its authority
over our people extended to wherever they might be. No
one, not even our Roman overlords, could thwart the desires of our high priests in matters of our faith.

It would be a simple matter, with my letters from
Caiaphas and others, introducing me to the synagogues
of Damascus, to ferret out these heretics who had fled
the Holy City to plant their troublesome seed in alien
soil. A little spying, a few denunciations followed by
quick arrests, and I should be on my way back to Jerusalem with a band of well-bound prisoners.

My next appearance before the Sanhedrin would be
in the nature of a triumph. Here, they would say, is the
gallant young soldier of the faith, returned from a brief
campaign with a train of dangerous captives.

How pleased Caiaphas would be! And in his daughter's dark and smiling eyes surely there would be a gleam
of favor, encouraging her doting father to admit me to
the priestly aristocracy!

As at this instant our caravan was passing from days
of desert drought and solitude into the smiling, rose-
decked suburbs of Damascus, even so it seemed to me
that I was passing from years of discipline and struggle
into the realization of my fondest hopes: into a position
of leadership and authority in the religion of my fathers,
with wealth and power and domestic bliss its natural
accompaniments.

*   *   *

These were my dreams when suddenly there came a blinding flash of light, brighter than ever the noonday sun had shone upon the desert.

I stumbled from my mount and fell prostrate in the dust, trembling with shock and fear.

"Saul, Saul," came a voice from I could not tell where, "why do you persecute me?"

"Who are you, my Lord?" I asked in my confusion, my very question revealing that I knew the dread answer.

"I am Jesus," came the reply, fulfilling all my fears. "I am Jesus whom you persecute. Ah, Saul, why do you fight against that which you know to be the right?"

It was true. All this plotting, this constant hatred, these murders and imprisonments; I had known that they were wrong. But like one under the spell of a magician I had gone on and on, persecuting, binding, killing. These words, so simple, so straightforward, had broken a spell that held me bound more tightly than any of my prisoners. In an instant I saw Truth, and yielded to its boundless power.

"Lord," I asked, still trembling and astonished, "what would you have me do?"

"Arise," came the answer. "Go into the city, and it will be told you what to do."

That was all. So little said. So much achieved. Quick, and sharper than a two-edged sword, the Word of God.

*   *   *

The caravan, thrown into confusion, had crowded around me. Some had seen the blinding flash, they said;

others had heard the voice; but only I had grasped the meaning of it all.

I stood up. I could see nothing, although my eyes were open. The light, that shining, glorious light, was still around me. I heard the voice of Jesus say:

"Saul, I have appeared to you to make you my minister, and my witness both as to these things which you have seen, and those things in which I will appear to you. I will save you both from the Jewish people and from the Gentiles, to whom I now send you to open their eyes, and to turn them from darkness to light, and from the power of Satan to God, that they may receive forgiveness for their sins, and an inheritance among those who are made holy through faith in me."

These words came to me as my companions in the caravan, disturbed by my continued blindness, were offering their hands to guide me into Damascus, and discussing what they might do to aid and comfort me.

Recalling the event, it is not lost upon me that here, in my extremity, I found the first evidence of loving-kindness that had been vouchsafed me for many months. These companions of my journey, puzzled though they were by these strange occurrences, did all they could to help me.

There had been no place for deeds of kindness in my life. It had been a life of scheming, of political intrigue, of bigotry and persecution. There had been no time for simple friendship; all was striving for a selfish goal, disguised as zeal for my religion.

These comrades of the Jerusalem road lifted me and

led me into the city, to the house of one Judas in the
street called Straight, a kindly man. They did not know
it—I did not know it then—but now it is clear to me that
their loving care was but the response to something I
had newly gained: a brotherly affection for my fellow
men. My brief vision of the Master, and the words I
heard, had given this quality to me, and those with
whom I came in contact felt it, even though they did
not recognize its source.

That was what happened to me, Saul of Tarsus, outside the gate of Damascus. It wrought a revolution in
my life.

*   *   *

Three days I stayed in Judas' house. They were three
days such as Jesus must have spent in the sepulcher, and
I came out from that house, even as Jesus came out from
the tomb, resurrected.

In those three days, I glimpsed something of the
meaning of what had happened to me on the Jerusalem
road. I saw the evil I had done, the hardness of my
heart, the sorry plight to which my base ambition had
led me.

I saw the meanness of the high priests' malice toward
the Nazarenes, the narrow bigotry of my own sect, the
Pharisees.

And over against these things, I saw and felt the uni-
versal love of God for all mankind, the broadness of His
mercy, the tenderness of His care for every creature, the
joy of living in His service.

I find that I can write of these things only in terms of vision, yet I was blind. My eyes, though open, saw no man. Withdrawn apart in Judas' house, I neither ate nor drank, yet did not suffer hunger nor thirst.

Reviewing the sad futility of my career, I pledged my life to the service of Christ. I, who had done such harm to the followers of the Nazarene, could do much good for them. My knowledge of the workings of the Jewish hierarchy might help me to shield these people from the high priests' wrath.

Yet with this blindness upon me, I felt that I should be much hampered in this work, and prayed God continually that this evil might be taken from me. Even as I prayed, there came a vision of a man entering my chamber, who put his hand upon me, and immediately it seemed my sight was restored to me. The name of the man, the vision told me, was Ananias.

Comforted by this assurance of God's care, I continued in prayer. On the third day, in fulfillment of this vision, a man entered the house of Judas and came to me, and putting his hands upon me, comforted me.

"Brother Saul," said he, "the Lord Jesus, who appeared to you on the road as you came, has sent me, that you may receive your sight, and be filled with the Holy Spirit."

His name, he said, was Ananias, and he was a disciple of Jesus.

Immediately as he spoke, my eyes were opened as if scales had fallen from them. My sight returned forthwith, and I arose and went with Ananias, to a place where the followers of Jesus in Damascus were gathered together. I was baptized as one of them. I supped with them, and my strength, which had forsaken me ever since the vision on the highway, returned to me and I was strong and vigorous, as before.

Then Ananias told us how he had been led to find me and to deliver me from my blindness. A voice had called to him by name as he slept.

"Here am I, Lord," he had replied when he recovered from his amazement.

"Arise," the voice commanded him, "and go into the street called Straight, and enquire at the house of Judas for one called Saul, of Tarsus: for he is praying and has seen in a vision a man named Ananias coming in, and putting his right hand on him, that he might receive his sight."

"Lord," Ananias had replied, "I have heard about this man from many people, what evil he has done to the saintly ones at Jerusalem. He has come here with authority from the chief priests to make prisoners of those who call upon the name of Jesus."

"Go nevertheless," the voice commanded Ananias, "for this man is my chosen instrument to carry my name to the Gentiles, and to kings, and to the children of Israel. For I will show him how great sufferings he must endure for my name's sake."

And Ananias, though trembling with fear for the cruel things that I might do to him, had done the Lord's bidding, with the results that have been told. It is but an example of the great truth that he who does the Lord's commands will achieve much good, and be shielded from all evil.

* * *

It has never been my way to waste precious hours. Hardly had I been baptized when I began to go into the synagogues to preach the words of Jesus. Into the very congregations where I had planned to spy and seize and kill these witnesses to the Son of God, I now went and paid tribute to Christ's name.

The Jews were astounded. They had heard of my activities in Jerusalem, and of my mission to Damascus to root out heresy.

"Is this not he," they asked each other in amazement, "who destroyed those who called upon Christ's name in Jerusalem, and who came here for the express purpose of bringing such offenders bound before the chief priests?"

They plied me with questions and tried to catch me in learned arguments, but with God's help I was able to refute their claims and confound them all. Their rage against me grew ever greater.

They invented wild tales about me, as, for example, that I was born a pagan, became a Jew in hope of wedding Caiaphas' daughter, and turned against the Jews because the high priest had refused me her hand. So base a slander I thought it not worth while to answer. Yet it has gained currency in the years that have passed since then, and it seems wise now expressly to deny it.

I was born not a pagan, but a Jew. I did aspire to the
hand of Caiaphas' daughter, and he appeared to encourage me in that design. Up to the moment of my
vision outside the gate of Damascus, it seemed that I
was destined to be a leader of the Jews. But from that
moment, everything was changed.

I did not turn against the Jews because Caiaphas refused me his daughter's hand; rather would Caiaphas
have refused me her hand because I had turned against
the Jews. After the change that came upon me, there
could have been no possibility of my joining the high
priests' faction, nor of forming any alliance with Caiaphas' family. From that moment I was already wedded:
wedded to the faith in Christ.

The Jews grew daily more angry with me, nor was I
welcomed as a convert by all the followers of Jesus.
Ananias and some of his friends indeed made me welcome, but there were others who feared me, suspecting
that I was still the spy of the Sanhedrin, feigning conversion to their faith to snare them more securely.

Hounded by the Jews, suspected by the disciples of
Jesus, I found myself in a sorry plight. I did not fear the
persecutors, but my very presence in Damascus brought
a storm of hatred upon the Nazarenes. The sight of me
preaching as their mouthpiece in the synagogues brought
down upon them such a torrent of wrath that I determined to go elsewhere. Seeing that my actions only injured those whom I would bless, I decided to withdraw.

A return to Jerusalem seemed unwise under these conditions. I cast about where I might go, and there came

to me the words which the Lord had spoken to me, and to Ananias, saying that I should go among the Gentiles.

Now here was I in the Gentile city of Damascus. The Gentile overlord of the city was Aretas IV, King of Arabia. To the south and east lay his kingdom, a desert land but sparsely settled, a land where one might find seclusion for prayerful thought and meditation.

I went into Arabia.

Three

——

SEVERAL reasons led me to venture into Aretas'
kingdom. First was the need of calm seclusion for a time, to ponder the magnitude of my decision,
and to plan a course of future action. Next was the
natural inclination that I had for travel, the desire always to visit places yet unseen—and Arabia, with its
rock-hewn capital at Petra, was a place of oft-told
legends.

Last, and most important, was the charge I had received to carry the glad tidings of Jesus to the Gentiles.
The kingdom of Aretas seemed the natural place to go,
seeing that, in the interest of my new-found brothers in
Christ, I must leave Damascus, and shield them thus
from further persecution.

That portion of Arabia where I went is called Arabia
Petraea, because it is a stony place, with only here and
there an oasis or watered valley among its barren, rocky
ridges.

It is sparsely inhabited by a people known as Naba-
taeans, an Arab race who have their own kingdom under
Aretas, their own religion, wherein they worship the god
Dhushara and the goddess Allat, and their own capital
city at Petra, which is assuredly one of the strangest cities
in the world.

Set in a deep canyon with steep walls of solid rock,
its principal approach is through a narrow cleft in the
canyon wall, hardly wide enough to let two chariots
pass, and therefore easy of defense.

The stone and mud houses stand closely confined in
the middle of the canyon floor, and since the space there
is limited, the town actually burrows into the cliffs on
either side. Here in the rose-red rock these Arabs have
carved many chambers for their dead, and some for other
uses, each entered by a door in the face of the steep
cliff. Around each door has been carved, with great skill
and precision, a dignified facade, not unlike the front
of a temple.

As a consequence of this practice, the canyon walls
on either side of Petra are honeycombed with chambers,
and adorned with magnificent rock carvings, where
Greek and Egyptian columns, and here and there a
Roman design, with clear-cut entablatures, dispute for
pre-eminence in a vast work of art.

Here in Aretas' capital city I lived for a time, then
wandered with the nomads in the surrounding desert,
living in tents such as it had been my craft to make in
Tarsus. My skill in making these tents endeared me to
the Arabs, and as I traveled with them through the

wilderness, sewing the coarse cilicium, or haircloth, into tents, I often told them the story of Jesus, and some few believed.

But here among the Arabs, no less than among the Jews of Palestine, were many who fought against Truth, and were bitter against me because I sought to wean them from their heathen gods.

There was much muttering against me in the tents, and word came from Petra that King Aretas was annoyed because there was among his people one who dared dispute the power and divinity of Dhushara and Allat.

I joined a caravan for Damascus, and soon was back among those who had befriended me at the time of my conversion: good Ananias, who had healed me of my blindness, and the rest. They welcomed me with kindliness, and again I spoke in the synagogues. God gave strength and conviction to my words, and the Jews who tried to dispute the truth of my teaching were confounded.

Yet now I had a double enemy to oppose me. The Jews were still embittered against me for what they called my treason, and the officers of King Aretas tracked me to the city. The king's governor in Damascus gave orders to the soldiers of his garrison to apprehend me, and placed a watch at all the gates of the city to seize me if I passed. I was beset on every hand, and my very presence there endangered the kind friends who harbored me. I decided again to leave the city.

One night, when all was still and only the stars shed

light upon the streets and gardens of Damascus, I was taken to the house of one of the disciples, which stood against the city wall. Certain of its balconied windows overhung the ramparts. The owner of the house had observed and noted the watches that were kept by the Arabian garrison, and knew the times when sentries passed that portion of the wall.

A large basket with a rope attached was ready just inside the trellised window of an upper room that overhung the wall. We gathered there in darkness. Soon we heard the tramp of a platoon of soldiers as they made the rounds outside the wall, relieving the guard. The muffled rhythm of their sandaled feet in the thick dust, the chink of arms and armor as they marched, came to us as they passed below our hiding-place.

Peering through the trellis, I could see them dimly, the conical caps and square-cut beards of the Arabian soldiery, the glint of starlight on steel weapons.

On they marched, a word of command was given by the officer of the guard, and they rounded a corner of the wall between us and the Jerusalem gate.

"Now is the time," whispered the owner of the house.

The window trellis was withdrawn, the basket with its stout rope attached was placed outside the opening. I hastily whispered my farewell to each of these faithful friends, giving them the kiss of peace.

Then I stepped into the basket and was gently lowered to the ground. I stepped out into the dusty road and waved my arm in farewell as the basket was cautiously drawn up through the window and the trellis closed.

Silently I stole away through the darkness to a friendly inn beyond the walls, where a place had been reserved for me. Next morning, I became a simple wayfarer in the steady stream of commerce that flowed along the Jerusalem road.

*   *   *

As I passed the place where Christ Jesus had appeared to me, I paused beneath a sheltering palm to ponder.

Three years had passed since that bright flash of heavenly light had brought me tumbling from my pinnacle of earthly pride, to realize my humble place in God's great plan of life.

Three hard but happy years, wherein strange contrasts had abounded. Men's hands had been turned against me as never before in my experience, yet I had enjoyed for the first time the true affection of brothers in the faith of Christ. My paths had lain in alien and pagan lands, among the Gentiles of Damascus and the heathens of Arabia, yet I was ever more conscious of the presence of God than I had been within the very confines of the temple at Jerusalem.

I had felt the comfort and rejuvenation of Truth, and broken the bread of Life with simple, kindly men in the squat, black tents of the desert. For this, the hands of all but a loving few had been turned against me.

Would it be always so? Must I, who might have been a ruler of the Jews, pass the remainder of my days a hunted creature, never free from the spying eyes of treacherous enemies?

I finally concluded, as I sat beneath that palm tree, that this mattered not at all. If enemies beset me, I must oppose them boldly, or better still, win them to my way of thought. Regardless of what might befall me, of hateful strife or unjust persecution, I must continue on my way—the only way of Life. Any other course was unthinkable.

I stepped again into the stream of travelers on the Jerusalem road.

Four

___

How strange it was, this return to Jerusalem! When I had left the Holy City, three years before, I had departed with hatred in my heart, seeking to build a career on the blood of harmless, gentle men and women.

Out through the gate where Stephen had been stoned I had come, and gloated over the deed done on this fateful spot. But now, as I approached the city, I turned my head in shame, and could not look at the harsh stones that lay, it seemed, where they had fallen at poor Stephen's feet.

I went into the city, but not to my old quarters near the high priest's house. Instead, I sought a humble lodging in the neighborhood where my fellow followers of Jesus made their homes.

Word had been sent to them by the brothers in Damascus of my coming, and I let my whereabouts be known to them, but received no invitation to be present at their meetings. They were still suspicious of me. The memory of my cruelties before I left Jerusalem lingered on, and made them doubt the sincerity of my conversion.

At last, Barnabas came to see me. He was a Jew, a Levite, from Cyprus, not many miles across the sea from my boyhood home at Tarsus. He had been rich in lands, but had sold his possessions and brought the money to lay at the feet of the disciples in Jerusalem, to be used for the common good.

His name was Joses, but they had named him Barnabas, meaning "son of consolation." The name seemed to me well chosen, for he brought me much consolation at this time when those I would have joined in Christly fellowship were kept away from me by fear.

Dear Barnabas, my first close friend, my companion on many a mile by land and sea, in perils and in joys! Was I too harsh with you when we came at last to parting of the ways? Might I not have been more patient, more kindly with you? Need we have parted when we did? Ah, Barnabas, I love you dearly, and still love you wherever you may be, in the land of the living or among those who have fallen asleep.

Barnabas came to my lodging and took me to meet such apostles as were in Jerusalem, but most of them at that time were absent from the city on various preaching missions. We found only Peter and James, the brother of Jesus.

Barnabas stood sponsor for me, telling them how I had seen the Lord in a vision at Damascus, how he had spoken to me and appointed me to preach the glad tidings to the Gentiles, and how I had preached boldly at Damascus in the name of Jesus.

Gradually their distrust of me departed, and I was received into fellowship with those who had so intimately known the Master. It was the first time that I had been privileged to meet with anyone who could tell in such detail the wondrous doings of our Lord.

Peter had been sobered by his experience when he had denied knowing Jesus, just before the crucifixion, but he was still a roaring torrent of missionary zeal, an ardent flame of faith that persecution could not dim. His gigantic fisherman's frame, his brusque yet kindly manner, his frankness and impetuosity of speech, made him a potent force among the followers of Jesus. I was to meet him again, at a crisis in the affairs of the church.

James, the eldest brother—or, as some said, half-brother—of Jesus, had now become the recognized spokesman of our congregation at Jerusalem. His rise to this position had been rapid, and somewhat unexpected. During the earthly ministry of Jesus, he had never joined the apostles, nor devoted himself to the furtherance of our faith. Only after the resurrection did he see the glory of the Master's way, and join himself to the apostles at Jerusalem.

Rather because of his relationship to the Master, than for any other reason—or so it seemed to me—he had been widely recognized as a leader in our congregation. He continued to observe many of the rules and practices of the Jews, and was on intimate terms with the Pharisees, who apparently believed he had a latent sympathy with their sect. This seemed strange to me, but appeared to matter little at the time.

I gave myself up completely to the inspiration that I gained from friendly consort with these two erstwhile companions of Jesus, and gained great strength and understanding from their discourses.

With this new zeal, I went into the synagogues and spoke. Into the very synagogue of the libertines, where I had helped to lure Stephen into the trap that had been laid for him, I went to preach the very words that Stephen had spoken there before me.

Before fifteen days had passed, I could feel the net that had snared Stephen being drawn about me. The Jews were furious with what they thought was my duplicity, and they began to lay their plans to deal with me as I had dealt with Stephen.

In my trouble, I went to the temple to pray, and as I prayed, a vision came again to me, not unlike that I had seen outside the gate of Damascus.

"Make haste," said the voice that had spoken to me before in my distress, "and get quickly out of Jerusalem, for they will not receive your testimony concerning me."

But I was loath to accept this warning. I did not wish to flee, and thus seem cowardly in the sight of men. I even hoped that, by my testimony, by calling attention to my own experience and my own conversion, I could bring the Jews to follow in my steps. I dared to argue with the Lord.

"Lord," said I, "they know that I imprisoned and

beat in every synagogue those who believed in you. When the blood of Stephen was shed, I was standing by, consenting to his death, and guarding the raiment of those who slew him."

But my argument was of no avail.

"Depart," came the voice again, "for I will send you far away among the Gentiles."

The command left no room for further argument nor hesitation. It was peremptory and absolute. And it confirmed, by divine revelation for the third time, that the field of my labors was to be not among the Jews in Jerusalem, but in wider fields, among Gentile populations.

I shared with Barnabas, Peter and James the revelation that had come to me, and they arranged for my prompt departure from Jerusalem.

As at Damascus, so in the Holy City, there were faithful disciples who could be called upon at need to transport a member of our congregation from the closing jaws of official persecution. Secretly they smuggled me down to the coast at Caesarea and aboard a boat bound for my native Tarsus.

As we unfurled our sails and glided smoothly out of the snug little harbor that Herod and the Romans had built beside their shining new city of white stone, I felt that I was taking a further step out of the environment of my ancestors and my young manhood.

"Farewell, Jerusalem," I whispered as, peering out from my hiding-place in the stern of the little vessel, I saw the coastline gradually recede behind us. "Fare-

well, Judea. Farewell, faith of my fathers. The last time
I left Jerusalem, I was led, at Damascus, to glimpse the
grandeur of a greater, purer faith. I brought it back with
me to Jerusalem, and tried to share it with my friends
of former days. But they would have none of it. Jerusalem would have none of it. Jerusalem would have killed
me, as I killed Stephen.

"I went into the temple, the center of our Jewish
faith, to pray for those who have turned against me, that
thcy, too, might be brought to see the light that I have
seen. And the answer to my prayer was, not an assurance
that Jerusalem will be converted, but a command to
leave Jerusalem and bring my message to the Gentiles.
Farewell, Jerusalem. Henceforth, my face is toward the
Gentiles. These peoples, whom you despise, may yet
become the cornerstone in the structure we are building.
My future lies among them."

It was not, of course, my last farewell to Jerusalem. I
was to come again into the Holy City. Yet this first
farewell marked a turning in my life from much that the
Judean capital stood for.

Henceforth, my steps led, with few exceptions, to
northward and to westward. Already, our faith was growing faster and taking better root in Gentile than in
Jewish lands. It has been my lot, by divine appointment,
to superintend its growth in ever new and wider territories.

Five

___

THAT it had been wise for me to leave Jerusalem was soon evident. Word came to me
in Tarsus that, as a result of my departure, the Jews had
for the moment relented in their persecution of the
church. Hearing that I had gone, their hatred lacked a
focus, and they were diverted to other things, with the
result that the churches throughout all Judea and Samaria and Galilee enjoyed a period of rest, and were
edified, and converts were rapidly multiplied.

Back in my boyhood home in Tarsus, I found myself
in familiar surroundings, but with a vast difference in
my outlook. I returned to my trade of tent-making, as
has always been my practice in time of need. It is an
honest craft, and I thank God that my good father had
the wisdom to see that his son was taught a trade. The
pursuit of it has often stood me in good stead.

The work of my hands was the same, but all else was

different. Gradually my change of faith became known
to my former associates in the market-place. Old Jewish
friends began to shun me, but a few listened to what I
had to say, and certain Gentiles grasped eagerly the
message that I brought.

Small groups began to gather to hear the words of
Jesus as they had been reported to me, and to marvel at
the story of his deeds. Not only in Tarsus, but in many
towns and villages of Cilicia and Syria, such gatherings
were held. Some of these groups became the nuclei of
churches. I traveled much throughout these territories,
sowing the good seed.

In Tarsus, I encountered not only the opposition of
the Jews and the cynicism of the pagans, but the hard,
cold intellectuality of the philosophic schools. As a
center of academic disputations, Tarsus was but slightly
less important than Athens or Alexandria.

Chief among these philosophers were the Stoics, whose
stern doctrines had much to commend them to men of
courage, but in whose scheme of life there was no place
for humility nor compassion. Their founder, Zeno, had
been born in this quarter of the world, in Cyprus, and
his teachings had taken especially firm root in Tarsus.
From Tarsus had come some of the most illustrious of
their school, including Athenodorus, tutor of the emperor Augustus, and Nestor, tutor of the emperor Tiberius.

When I had lived in Tarsus as a lad, a Jew, I had
hardly been aware of their existence; but now as the
apologist of a new religion, I came often into contact

with them. Their pride, their fatalistic hardness of heart, made them difficult of approach. I tried to batter down this wall of separation, but with little success. One cannot easily talk of the love of God with men whose ambition is to hold coldly aloof from any feeling of human or divine affection.

The church of God, I learned at Tarsus, is not to be built upon the systems of arrogant philosophers.

In spite of the indifference and open enmity that I found in Tarsus, much good was gained. Not the least of my achievements was the winning over to the way of Christ of my good sister and her little son. Henceforth, I could feel that some of my nearest kinsfolk had been joined to me with bonds even stronger than those of blood.

Twenty years later, my sister's son, grown to young manhood, saved my life, as I shall recount in due time.

My work in Tarsus and the surrounding country continued several years, and bore much fruit. I was happy in it, and expected to continue indefinitely in that region, when suddenly came such a change as God often interposes in the plans of men.

My good friend Barnabas, who had introduced me to Peter and James at Jerusalem, and dispelled the fear that the apostles had of me, appeared in Tarsus with tidings that called for prompt action.

"Come with me at once to Antioch," said Barnabas, "for you are greatly needed there."

And he went on to explain how our faith had prospered in that city, the capital of Syria, until there was need for leaders of wisdom and experience to guide the flock. Barnabas himself had been sent there by the elders at Jerusalem for this purpose. He found his labors even heavier than he had expected and, needing assistance, he had thought of me, not far away in Tarsus; for word of my preaching in Cilicia had come to him in Antioch.

Now the reason for this rapid growth of the church in Antioch is worthy of note. It came about, in part, as a result of the persecutions I had organized in Jerusalem against Stephen and others, several years before. Some of those who had fled before my wrath from Jerusalem had found their way not only to Damascus, where I intended to pursue them, but also to Cyprus and Phoenicia and Antioch.

Arriving in these places, they continued to preach the gospel, but to Jews only, as was their practice at that time. Yet some of them were Jews who, like myself, had come originally from Gentile cities in Syria and elsewhere. Inevitably, their message came to the ears of Gentiles as well as of Jews, and soon a considerable number of Greeks and Syrians had joined themselves to our congregations.

When the apostles in Jerusalem heard of this, they were much concerned lest the pure teaching of the Christ might become polluted through passing into Gentile hands. They therefore sent Barnabas, who was himself from Cyprus, and who knew the Gentile way of life, to Antioch to supervise the preaching of the Word.

When Barnabas arrived at Antioch, he rejoiced to find that Truth was being taught in all its purity, and that

Gentiles as well as Jews were rallying to our cause. He exhorted them all to cleave to the Lord, and being a good man, full of the Holy Spirit and of faith, he gathered about him a multitude of followers.

The rapid growth of the congregation in Antioch, and the need of assistance in his work, led him to seek me out and enlist my aid.

"Come with me," said Barnabas. And I immediately left all and followed him to Antioch.

This metropolis of Syria, and indeed of the whole East, is at once the loveliest and the most terrible city that I have seen in all my travels. Situated on the banks of the river Orontes, and on an island in that river, it abounds in gardens and palaces and heathen shrines. Nature has made it rich and beautiful, and man has lavished upon it all his art and skill in building.

A fortress and a temple to the Romans' false god Jupiter crown a mountain that overlooks the city. At its foot a broad avenue, lined on either side with covered colonnades and porticoes, extends the full four miles across the city's width, from wall to wall.

The climate is delightful, conducive to outdoor games and festivals, and the populace seems to be concerned only with amusing itself in the most sinful and extravagant manner. Horse and chariot races take place almost daily, and the city divides itself into factions, known as the Greens and the Blues, each in support of its favorite on the race-course; riots between these factions are but a part of this wild entertainment.

A rabble of Greeks and Syrians, with a sprinkling of

the scum of every Eastern Mediterranean port, lives in an atmosphere of feverish excitement, wasting in wagers on the races the meager but sufficient living that the natural riches of the city afford to all.

This ignorant and profligate populace is preyed upon by evert sort of impostor and mountebank. Soothsayers and astrologers, and every variety of magician that the East spews forth, find there a gullible audience, and a ready and profitable market for their tawdry wares.

In the luxuriant suburb of Daphne, a shrine to the heathens' false god Apollo serves as a focus for festivals which have never been surpassed in sinfulness and vice.

Into this beautiful but profligate and vicious city came Barnabas and I, and joined the growing band of true worshipers who, almost unnoticed in the hectic rush of this mad scramble for riches and amusement, were nevertheless engaged in affairs much more momentous than even the most notorious of its citizens.

As we walked along the sculptured arcades, I marveled at the beauty of the place and wondered that such loveliness could be combined with such appalling sin and vice. The city's beauty was a spell. It cast its charm over the beholder like a magician's thrall. The citizenry walked entranced in soft somnambulism, yielding themselves unthinkingly to every impulse of the senses.

We came to a place where an arcade, and several villas adjoining it, lay in ruins. An atmosphere of melancholy, a gentle and almost winning melancholy, here prevailed.

"And what has happened here?" I asked of Barnabas.

"How is it that amidst all this splendor there should be ruins?"

"Two earthquakes," he replied, "have in recent years laid certain portions of the city low. The people, enchanted with their pleasures, have not troubled to rebuild, but in their easy fashion have left some portions lie in ruins, excusing themselves from labor on the ground that, even in ruins, their city is more fair than any other. They say, too, that their gods, who have chosen thus to display their power, might be offended if these buildings were restored."

"Ah, Barnabas," said I, "I see indeed that you and I, and those who labor with us here, have much to do to waken these poor folk from the spell of ease and ignorance that lies so heavily upon them."

As we labored, we found that there were many in all walks of life who, wearied with unsatisfying pleasures and amusements, were seeking a truer, more substantial way of living. Gentiles, in even greater numbers than Jews, abandoned their vain pursuits and joined them-selves to our little community.

Gradually it became evident to even the most casual observer that we were not merely a sect of the Jews, as many had thought of us, but a separate congregation with a faith of our own.

The wags of Antioch—famous for the sharp sarcasm of their ridicule—found a name for us. They began to call us "Christians," scoffing in the Roman idiom at our willingness to be the followers of one whom the Jews refused to recognize as their Christ, or Messiah.

We took the title to ourselves, glorying in the name that had been given us in ridicule. At Antioch and at this time we were first called Christians.* The name will forever be our proud possession.

Barnabas and I had labored for a year together when again there came a call that could not be ignored. The church at Antioch was well grounded, and it was becoming prosperous. Our ministrations had reached to almost every element in the population, and many came to us bearing gifts. Money that had formerly been squandered at the races served through us to relieve deserving ones who had fallen into distress.

I sometimes felt that a greater danger lay in our becoming too rich, than in remaining poor. There were vast riches in the city, and those who felt our healing ministry gave freely to our cause. Soon we had enough and to spare, for our needs were simple.

Just at this juncture came a call for help which we were well equipped to meet. In Antioch arrived a mission from the apostles in Jerusalem, led by one Agabus, with reports of impending famine in Judea.

The news was received with concern even by those who had been Gentiles, and who had never visited Jerusalem; for all felt a close kinship with the disciples in the Holy City.

Each of us agreed to contribute, according to his ability, to a fund for succoring the Christian community in Judea. A collection was promptly taken and Barnabas

* 44 A.D.

and I were delegated to take the fund, or the supplies to
be purchased with it, to Jerusalem.

Without delay we set off on our errand of mercy,
the first of this sort in which I had a share, but not the
last. For the church at Jerusalem, by reason of persecution, or of famine, was often in distress, and it fell to
my lot more than once to raise money and supplies for
its relief.

I have always welcomed an opportunity to do this
service, not only because it is a humane and kindly act,
but because it serves to knit more closely the various
elements in our church. It is a practical recognition that
there is neither Jew nor Gentile in the sight of God.
The spectacle of those who have been Gentiles sending
aid to those who have been Jews is convincing evidence
of our unity.

In Jerusalem, Barnabas and I found the church in
dire distress. Not only was there hardship from lack of
food, both among Jews and Christians, but the Christian
community had just been subjected to cruel persecution.
Two of the twelve original apostles had borne the brunt
of this attack.

James, the brother of John, had been beheaded by
King Herod Agrippa I, and Peter had been cast into
prison. James was lost to us forever, but Peter was
promptly freed from his imprisonment by the angel of
the Lord and the prayers of the apostles. King Herod,
as if in retribution for his attack upon us, died almost
immediately of a foul disease.

Our arrival with a gift of grain from Antioch restored

the courage of the disciples at Jerusalem, whose faith had been sorely tried. We delivered our goods and money into the hands of the elders and took our leave for Antioch. Both Barnabas and I were eager to return to our labors there, which we had abandoned only at the request of our fellow Christians, in order to bring aid to Jerusalem.

With us on our return to the Syrian capital came a young kinsman of Barnabas, named Mark.

Barnabas was eager for the lad to come with us, and I yielded to his request. The young man's mother, Mary, was a matron of Jerusalem whose house was always open to the disciples. The elders often gathered there, particularly in times of danger or of stress, for Mary was a person of influence and under her roof there was a certain measure of security. It was to her house that Peter rushed when, on the night that the angel liberated him from prison, he found himself suddenly free. Young Mark told us the story on the journey to Antioch.

"We were all gathered together in a large upper room in mother's house," he said, "praying for Peter. King Herod had just put James to death, and we feared lest Peter might be the next to go. We comforted each other with accounts of how each of us had been delivered, through God's loving care, from hardships of every sort, and prayed individually and in unison for Peter.

"Late in the night, as we were praying and softly singing hymns, my mother's maidservant, Rhoda, rushed into the room in great excitement, crying, 'Peter is at the gate!'

" 'The girl is mad,' we said, and told her to be quiet.

"But she insisted that she had heard a knock at the gate and had gone to listen there, and that she had recognized Peter's voice.

" 'I was so glad,' she said, 'that I have come at once to tell you.'

"Unbelieving still, we surmised whether Peter might not already have been put to death, and whether the maid might not have heard the voice of his spirit.

"Yet she was so much in earnest, that some of us went down with her to the gate. There was someone knocking there. We threw open the door, and there stood Peter.

"As we embraced him with shouts of joy, he placed a finger on his lips, cautioning us to be quiet. We hurried him into the upper room, where all present wept with joy at his deliverance, as he told us how the angel had come into his prison cell, freed him from the chains that bound him to his guards, and led him past the warders and out the gate, which opened of its own accord.

"Then Peter said to us, 'Go, tell these things to James the brother of Jesus and to the other disciples who are not here.' And Peter himself slipped away into hiding without telling us where he was going.

"Next morning there was great commotion at the prison, and in the garrison that had supplied the guard the night before. But no trace could be found of Peter. Herod was furious. He ordered the warden to be put to

death, and he might have turned his vengeance upon
us all, but he was just then called to Caesarea on some
business that he had with the Phoenicians. A few days
later, he was dead."

The lad told the story well, and Barnabas had great
hopes for him as a preacher. I hear it said that now, after
these many years, he is engaged in writing down all that
can be gathered of the sayings and deeds of the Master.*

Ah, Mark, I rejoice that you have been faithful.
There was a time when I had little hope for you, when
you appeared to me to be false to your high trust. But
that is in the past. It matters little now, since you are
true to what the Master taught.

We had not been long in Antioch when again there
came a summons to travel. A vision appeared to the
elders of the church as they met to worship, and the
voice of the Holy Spirit once more was heard.

"Set apart for me Barnabas and Saul," came the divine
command, "for the work that I have called them to do."

Now it had been revealed to me no less than three
separate times that my appointed task was to bring the
message of Truth to the Gentiles, and Barnabas likewise
had been engaged in the same work. We took this revelation as a summons to be about our missionary tasks,
and prepared at once to embark for new fields of enterprise.

The congregation at Antioch, after fasting and offering prayers for us, blessed us and sent us on our way.

* The Gospel According to St. Mark.

Thus began my first major missionary journey. I had already traveled much in Palestine, Arabia, Cilicia and Syria; henceforth my labors were to call me ever farther afield in the service of our Lord and Master.

Six

THIS, the first and least extensive of my three major missionary journeys, was to lead me from Antioch by sea to the island of Cyprus, thence to the mainland in the north and through the provinces of Pamphylia, Pisidia and Lycaonia; then back by sea to Antioch.

It did not, like my later journeys, lead me westward into Europe. It was a first step in my missionary enterprise, an exploratory journey which prepared the way for wider travels yet to come.

It abounded in adventure. It comprised, among other events, my conversion of a Roman governor; my formal change of name from Saul to Paul; the defection of Mark from his high calling; my first experience of being worshiped as a god; my first experience of being stoned almost to death, and my instantaneous recovery from my injuries by God's good grace; my first meeting with

49

Timothy, whom I love to call my son in the faith; and
a wide variety of minor adventures, cruel persecutions
and glorious victories over evil.

The first stage of our journey was the brief sail to
Cyprus. Barnabas, who went with me, was a native of
this island, and therefore especially helpful as a guide
and sponsor.

With us, at Barnabas' request, came his youthful kinsman, Mark—an arrangement which I protested at the
first, and one which proved to be unwise.

Our little ship called first at Salamis, near the eastern
end of the island. Going ashore here, we tarried briefly,
and preached the Word of God in the synagogues of
the Jews, then crossed the island to the city of Paphos,
capital of the Roman governor.

Here we were plunged at once into such a situation
as we had not yet encountered. Paphos was a melting-
pot of languages, peoples and religious sects. There were
many Greeks, a considerable colony of Jews, and a
Roman garrison, with a sprinkling of Asiatic folk. Greek
was the language of the educated citizens, Latin was the
official language of the governor's little court, and almost
every dialect of the Eastern Mediterranean lands was to
be heard in the bazaars.

Likewise, there was a great mixture of religions, but
the chief among them was the worship of Venus. Paphos
was no less a shrine of this false deity than Antioch's
suburb, Daphne, was a shrine of Apollo.

On this coast, according to legend, the beautiful goddess had first landed when she arose from the sea. Pil-

grims by thousands visited her shrine, passing in gay
processions from the new town on the seashore to the
ancient town, or shrine, several miles distant. These
festivals, like those of Apollo at Daphne, were often but
carnivals of lust.

The Paphian Venus had taken on peculiarities of her
own; the images of her that the priests sold had somewhat the aspect of a Phoenician or Assyrian deity.

Not all the people of Paphos were devoted to this
goddess, nor content to worship at her shrine. A variety
of Asiatic cults were spawned here by wandering magicians and soothsayers: Egyptians, Syrians, Chaldeans,
Jews. No tale was too preposterous to hang a cult upon;
and gullibility reached its apex among a people who had
no firm foundation for their faith.

Chief among these sorcerers and false prophets was a
renegade Jew, one Bar-jesus, who had taken to himself
the Arabic name of Elymas, meaning "The Wise." He
had gained a hold upon the rabble, but was in search of
bigger game, and did not hesitate to spin his web around
the Roman governor, or proconsul, Sergius Paulus. By
every sort of base flattery and mean intrigue the impostor
worked his way into the governor's circle and curried
the favor of officialdom.

But Sergius Paulus was a prudent man who, feeling
the need of some spiritual meat such as could not be
provided by the heathen cults, refused to yield himself
completely to the mystic maunderings of this artful
wretch. He heard of the activities of myself and Barnabas, and gave commandment that we should present our-

selves at the proconsular villa. He desired, he said, to
hear the Word of God.

Bar-jesus heard of this and was on hand before us.
When we were ushered into the audience chamber, there
was the sorcerer, doing his silly tricks of sleight-of-hand,
trying to impress the governor with his so-called super-
natural powers.

"My Lord," we heard him say as we entered the hall,
"you should yield yourself to my guidance in these deep
and mysterious matters. I call upon all the wisdom of
the East to guide me, and would gladly point out to you
the omens that are favorable, or unfavorable, for any
enterprise. Trust in Elymas, The Wise, and fortune will
attend you. Look not to these vagabond Christians for
any good, for they are but foolish children, unworthy
of your notice."

I did not hesitate. Striding boldly to the foot of the
dais on which the governor sat in his chair of state, I
fixed my eyes on Bar-jesus with all the firmness that I
could summon, seeing through the rottenness of his
stupid clowning.

"You who are full of craftiness and mischief," I thundered at him, "you child of the devil, you enemy of all
righteousness, will you not cease to pervert the ways of
the Lord? Now, at this instant, the hand of the Lord is
upon you. You shall be blind for a time, unable even
to see the light of day."

The words had come to me by inspiration; they recalled my own experience outside the gate of Damascus,

when I was blinded by the brightness of the vision that changed my way of life.

Immediately mist and darkness descended upon Bar-jesus, and he staggered about the audience chamber seeking someone to lead him by the hand.

Sergius Paulus, the governor, looked on in astonishment.

"Indeed," said he, "I believe in the doctrine which you teach, that can work such wonders upon its enemies."

Thus, as one of the first results of my journey, a powerful Roman official was added to the ranks of our believers. Truth began to permeate the official and public, as well as the private, life of the people of Cyprus.

This contact with Roman officialdom, and the growing consciousness that my work lay among the Gentiles, led me now to abandon my Hebrew name of Saul and to make use of the Roman name Paulus, or Paul. It was not uncommon for Jews who lived among the Gentiles to adopt Greek or Roman names, nor for the same person to have both a Hebrew and a Gentile name.

The transition from Saul to Paul was simple and natural, and by a happy coincidence my Roman name was the same as that of Sergius Paulus, whom I had been privileged to lead into the Christian fold. Moreover, the new name has always seemed appropriate, since the Latin word *paulus* means small, and I am short of stature. The name serves to remind me, when I am tempted by pride, that I am, after all, but the least among the humble servants of God.

Likewise, the affliction, or thorn that I carry in my

flesh, keeps me from exalting myself above measure. Yet I do not dwell overmuch upon this slight affliction, for I do not desire to magnify it as a handicap.

As a result of the conversion of the governor, we lived in honor in Cyprus, free from persecutions that I had experienced in Damascus, Arabia, Jerusalem and elsewhere. The faith took firmer root than ever in the island, and we might have lingered there in pleasant security. But in this work there is no place nor time for lingering.

Soon we were off again on our travels, Barnabas and I, and Mark came with us. But the youth did not stay long in our company.

Hardly had we landed at Perga, on the mainland of Pamphylia, after a short sail from Paphos, when he announced that he was returning to Jerusalem. The reason he would not name, but I fancy it was homesickness. He longed for his mother's hospitable house, where he might be with his fond parent and among old friends.

A ship in the harbor at Perga happened to be sailing soon for Caesarea; Mark went aboard it and departed for his home. He was, perhaps, still too young to face the hardships of a missionary life, and the bonds of home and family were too strong for him.

Barnabas and I kept resolutely on. Our way now lay inland through a rugged and inhospitable country. From sea level at Perga, we had to make the hard, long climb onto the high plateau of Asia Minor.

Beginning our journey across the fertile coastal plain, we soon began to rise into the foothills. Luxuriant fields and gardens gave way to oak-dotted slopes where sheep and cattle grazed. Then, with the ramparts of a mountain range rising sharply in front of us, we passed through a narrow, rocky defile and proceeded up a deep canyon with a tempestuous river racing down it. It crossed and recrossed our path; in places there were fords, and in others bridges.

Laurel and crimson oleander lined the river's bank in its more quiet stretches. Pines and firs rose high above us, and through the dark green of their upper branches we caught a glimpse, now and again, of snowy peaks. The air grew cooler as we mounted.

We came upon a caravan of families, making their annual migration, with their flocks of sheep, from the lowland country to the mountain valleys for the summer. We joined ourselves with them, and were glad of this companionship, for this was wild country. Many were the tales of brigands told around the campfires which we built each night, as we bivouacked in the open, or in caverns in the canyon walls.

But no robbers set upon us, and in time we came to the summit of a pass and then descended slightly to a lofty table-land which stretched for many miles to north and east, broken only here and there by mountainous outcroppings.

On this plateau, near the shore of a beautiful lake and at the foot of a range of mountains, lay the city of Antioch in Pisidia—not to be confused with Antioch, the capital of Syria, which I have already described. Being a colony, or military outpost, of Rome, the city has a strongly Roman character. Its buildings and its coinage bear the stamp of Roman rule, and a garrison is stationed there.

Here, as in all the Greek and Roman cities of the East, there was a group of Jewish traders, with a synagogue. I made it my practice to preach first to the Jews and then, if they rejected me, to turn to the Gentiles. This I was led to do in the Pisidian Antioch.

Barnabas and I went on the Sabbath to the synagogue. We observed all the customs and formalities of the Jewish worship. Entering the building, each of us placed over his head the four-cornered veil, or tallith, the badge of an Israelite, and found seats in one of the rows of benches that extended around the building.

We listened to the prayers as they were recited by the appointed official—called the angel, or apostle, of the assembly—and then to the reading of the law by the reader, as selected from the sacred roll of manuscript taken from the ark or chest on the side of the building closest to Jerusalem. After the law, the reader read selections from the writings of the prophets. Then the scroll was rolled up and returned to the proper official, or minister, to be returned to its place of safe-keeping in the ark.

When the reader had finished this portion of the service, the rulers or elders of the synagogue, who had noticed the presence of strangers, sent a message around to us.

"Brothers," they said, "if you have any word of encouragement for the people, let us hear it."

Being thus invited, I arose and spoke to them of our

common heritage: how our fathers were brought out of the land of Egypt and through the wilderness into the promised land; how they had been ruled first by judges and then by kings; of the prophecies of the coming of our Savior, Jesus, and of his advent; how the rulers of the Jews at Jerusalem had condemned and crucified him, and how he had risen from the dead.

"We declare to you," I said in conclusion, "the glad tidings that God has fulfilled to us, the children, the promise that was made to our fathers, for he has raised up Jesus again. And through this man the forgiveness of sins is announced to you."

And I warned them against refusing to believe these glad tidings.

The service closed with a benediction and an "Amen." After it was over, and many of the leading Jews had left the synagogue, other Jews, along with some proselytes and even some Gentiles who had been present, gathered around me and urged that I should repeat, on the next Sabbath and for a larger congregation, the things that I had said.

But some of the Jews were envious of my success, especially as many Gentiles flocked to hear my preaching. They set about contradicting my sayings and blaspheming against Truth.

Thereupon, Barnabas and I spoke boldly and frankly to them.

"It was necessary," we said to them, "that the Word of God should first have been spoken to you, but since you put it from you, and judge yourselves unworthy of everlasting life, we naturally turn to the Gentiles. For so the Lord has commanded us, saying, 'I have made you a light to the Gentiles, in order that you may bring salvation to the very ends of the earth.' "

This greatly pleased our Gentile followers, and they glorified the Word of God and published it throughout that entire region.

The unbelieving Jews, however, started a systematic persecution of us and our followers.

They found a way of working through the women of the congregation. I had noticed in the synagogue that, in the section reserved for women behind a latticed partition, there was a large gathering of female listeners.

Now, some of the leading Jewish women knew the wives of influential Gentile citizens. They told idle tales and circulated false versions of the things that I had said, intimating that Barnabas and I would cause trouble in the city.

Largely as a result of their silly gossip, the chief men of the city became alarmed and shortly obtained an order from the authorities commanding us to leave the city and its neighborhood.

This was my first experience—but not the last—of the trouble that women can bring to such a cause as ours if they are not subjected to loving guidance and discipline.

Further evidence of this danger was brought to my attention—and very forcibly—in the city we visited next after our expulsion from Antioch.

Shaking off the dust of this Pisidian city from our feet, we went directly to Iconium. And here we had much the same experience as at Antioch.

As I preached to the congregation assembled in the house of one of our friends, it happened that a maid named Thekla sat beside the window of her mother's house, adjoining that one where I was, and listened to my words.

I knew nothing of her being there until, one day, a rich young man whose name was Thamyris appeared before me, charging me with turning his betrothed against him, and threatening to hand me over to the governor for punishment.

At this I was amazed.

"I do not know what you mean," I told him. "Will you explain?"

"You have bewitched my loved one, Thekla," he cried, "and by your words have won her from me. Day and night she sits beside her window listening to your words, or waiting to hear the sound of your voice. When I entreat her to smile upon me as of yore, her gaze is fixed upon the house where you are preaching. Neither will she listen to her mother's promptings, but sits entranced, enraptured with your voice."

This young man, consorting with unbelieving Jews who would have put me out of the synagogue, and with unfaithful men among my followers, plotted to catch Barnabas and me by stealth, and stone us to death. I tried to reason with him, to show him that I had no designs upon his sweetheart, but in vain. Thekla, he claimed, continued enraptured by my teachings, and indifferent to him.

Then, one night not long afterward, the maid came to see me at my lodgings. She had bribed the watchman whom Thamyris and her mother had set at the door of her house by giving him her bracelets, and to the brother in whose house I slept she offered, if he would but let her enter, a silver mirror.

"The maid Thekla desires to see you," my host reported, telling me of her offer.

"Let her enter," I told him. It seemed best to see her and try to impress her with the error of her way.

Coming to my chamber, she threw herself at my feet.

"Tell me, O holy man," she sobbed, "the great things of God."

She listened in rapt attention to all that I said, and covered my hands and feet with kisses.

"O saintly one," she cried, "grant that I may stay with you, and go wherever you may go."

She was extremely fair, and so earnest were her entreaties that I was sorely tempted. What sweet companionship, I thought, she might afford me in my weary way!

But this was only for a moment. God warned me of the evil that might come of such a step. I would not take Thamyris' loved one from him, nor lure her from her mother's house to follow me along my stony road. Alone I must travel. There was no place in my way of life for such an earthly attachment; our Lord had trod a lonely path, and so must I.

"Fair Thekla," I said to her, "you are but a child. You cannot come with me. Go home to your mother's house, and to Thamyris, who loves you."

Slowly, weeping, she left the chamber. She did not return to her home, but wandered here and there, praising God in her peculiar fashion, giving evidence of a virgin freshness that often brought wonder to those who met her.

Strange tales are told of her adventures. I do not vouch for them. Some she has told me since, when we have met at Antioch, or at Myra. At intervals she has crossed my path, sometimes when least expected. Always she has showered me with affection, sought to exercise upon me her distinctive charm. Her presence, as I have traveled, has often been felt rather than seen. It is like a strain of distant music, a weird accompaniment that haunts the tenor of my way. I shall have more to say of her.

The plot of the angry Thamyris, and of the rulers of the Jews, to seize Barnabas and me, was ripening fast. We saw its imminence, and fled to Lystra.

Here, from being less than dust beneath the feet of the Iconians, we were suddenly cast in the role of gods. This swift change came about as follows.

That Lystra was a thoroughly heathen city we were well aware, both from its reputation and from the fact that, as we approached it, we found its most prominent building to be a temple to Jupiter, placed directly in front of the city's principal gateway.

Nevertheless, we preached the Word with great success, and found the Gentiles of this city more receptive to our teaching than the bigoted Jews who had persecuted us at Antioch and Iconium.

One day, as I was preaching in the market-place, I noticed, seated on the ground at the side of the crowd of listeners, a cripple. He had never been able to walk, his friends told me, from the time that he was born.

I was struck by the earnestness with which he listened to my words, and by the light of devotion that shone in his eyes. At the end of my discourse, I was led to approach him, feeling that he had faith to be healed, and turned my gaze upon him with all the compassion that I felt for him.

"Stand upright on your feet," I commanded him in a loud voice.

And he, freed by the divine power of my command from the bonds that had held him, leaped up and walked.

The people gathered about were astonished. A great chatter of voices arose, as the observers gave vent to their surprise in the mixed language of their native province.

"The gods have come down to us in the likeness of men!" they exclaimed.

They took Barnabas, who was big and benign in appearance, to be the embodiment of the patron god of their city, Jupiter; and me they took to be Jupiter's constant companion, messenger and spokesman, Mercury.

Absurd as this may seem, it was easy for them to believe, for there were many legends concerning visits which these two supposed deities had made to this very countryside, and they thought it only natural that their patron among the gods should choose to favor with his presence a city that was so devoted to his worship. As for me, they found me eloquent, and knew that I had traveled far and wide, and both these qualities were supposed to be characteristics of their Mercury.

Barnabas and I did not at first grasp the full extent of their mistaken belief, nor attach much importance to their superstition. We returned to the house where we were staying, considering that the incident was closed.

Our surprise can be imagined when, shortly afterward, there appeared at the gateway of our courtyard a great crowd, escorting the chief priest of the temple of Jupiter which we had seen at the city's gate, bringing oxen and garlands and all the paraphernalia of a pagan sacrifice to do us honor.

He was prepared, and the people were urging him on, to kill the beasts and offer up sacrifice to us as gods at our own gate.

When we understood what was taking place, we were dismayed, and rent our garments with grief and humiliation, and rushed out among the crowd, trying to dissuade the people from their foolish enterprise.

"Good sirs," we cried, "why do you do these things? We are but men, with natures like your own; we preach to you that you should turn from these vain practices to the living God, who made heaven, and earth, and the sea, and all things that are therein."

Reasoning with them thus, we finally, but with great difficulty, prevented them from offering sacrifice to us as gods.

Perplexed and disappointed, the mob dispersed, and the priest of Jupiter turned and drove his garlanded cattle away to his temple at the city gate.

It was a strange experience, the only time in all my long career that anyone has sought to worship me with formal sacrifices. The incident revealed the base ignorance and superstition of the Lycaonians, which was so strangely mingled with receptivity and enlightenment.

The people, disillusioned and confused, became a prey to fears and suspicions concerning us. It puzzled them that we should deny that we were gods. If we were not gods, then anyone who could do the wonders we had done must indeed be devils, or at least magicians.

They were aided in this reasoning by unbelieving Jews who had stealthily followed us from Antioch and Iconium, and who spread false tales of our doings in those cities. Since we had eluded their plots to kill us in their own cities, these evil men schemed how they might persuade the men of Lystra to murder us, as they had failed to do.

They so far succeeded that, one day as I walked alone through the streets of Lystra, they set upon me and beat me and stoned me, before I could recover from my surprise at their sudden onslaught.

At one moment, I was pursuing my way in peace, my thoughts upon the holy work I had to do. Yet in the next I was surrounded by screaming wretches who hurled great stones at me. I fell to the ground. Their raging figures grew dim. Then all was dark, and silence reigned.

When I awoke, I was lying on the ground outside the city wall. Several of our communion were gathered round me, ministering to my needs, washing my wounds. Beyond them were faces of the curious, and some were scowling.

"He is not dead," I heard someone say. "We dragged him out of the city, supposing he was dead."

I inwardly gave thanks to God for my deliverance, and even as I prayed I felt my strength return.

I arose and stood erect, and found that I could walk. Surrounded by my friends, who greatly rejoiced in my resurrection, and followed by a wondering throng of lookers-on, I walked home through the city gate, past the towering temple of Jupiter.

"When, O Jupiter," I silently asked as I passed by, "have you given such evidence of your love for man as to raise him from the dead?"

*   *   *

Next day, Barnabas and I left Lystra for Derbe. We departed from the city with mingled feelings of relief and sadness. There the glory of God had been shiningly demonstrated in the healing of the lame man, in my own resurrection from what seemed certain death, and in the founding of a Christian congregation. But there still hung over the city a cloud of ignorance and superstition that seemed almost impenetrable.

Yet I could rejoice that a good seed had been sown there in the household of one who has been dear to me for many years, my own son in the faith, my Timothy. For it was on this first visit of mine to Lystra that I was brought into close friendship with his grandmother Lois and his mother Eunice, and the young man himself was added to my flock, so that when I returned a year or two later I found him a leader among his fellow Christians there.

Ah, my dear Timothy, how much you have meant to me in all these years between! How sweet your comforting friendship, even now!

Barnabas and I went on to Derbe, where we preached with success to many listeners. This marked the extreme limit of our travels on this, our first journey. From there, we retraced our steps by the way that we had come, passing in disregard of dangers through Lystra, and Iconium, and Antioch in Pisidia, and then descending to the sea again at Perga, where we had landed in coming from Cyprus.

In all these cities, as we revisited them briefly, we encouraged the disciples and exhorted them to continue in the faith. We ordained elders in each church, and prayed and fasted.

Finally, from Perga's port of Attalia, we took ship for Antioch, whence we had started on our journey. And

when we had arrived safely there, we gathered the church
together and told them how God had worked through
us, and had opened the door of faith to the Gentiles.
And here we stayed a long time with the disciples.

Seven

O UR WORK was proceeding well in Antioch, and our church was growing steadily, when we were again confronted with the old problem of the relations between Judaism and our religion. Could only those who had been Jewish, at least in faith, become true Christians? Or could Gentiles who had never become Jewish proselytes step immediately into the Christian communion?

For me, there had never been any doubt on this point. I had for years been preaching directly to the Gentiles, and welcoming into our congregations even those who had never had any sympathy with the Jewish theology or way of life.

The question came to a focus in Antioch when certain of our more Pharisaical brothers from Jerusalem paid a visit to the city and criticized the freedom of our activities in this respect. At first, these false disciples steadily spied out the ground and acted in secret.

"Unless you have been circumcised according to the custom of Moses, you cannot be saved," they told some of our Gentile converts.

This caused great perplexity and distress among our newer adherents. Barnabas and I, discovering the troublemakers, talked earnestly with them, but they were adamant in their conviction. The situation became more and more disturbed, and harmful to the growth of our congregation.

Eventually, it was agreed that Barnabas and I, with a few others of the Antioch congregation, should go up to Jerusalem to discuss this question with the apostles and the elders there, and try to reach an agreement that would restore harmony in our churches.

I felt that the voice of God had counseled such a move. Before leaving on our mission, we adjured the church to continue constantly in prayer for the peaceful settlement of this dispute.

We went this time by land, through Phoenicia and Samaria, and on our journey through these Gentile nations we were confirmed in our assurance that God is no respecter of persons, and that his word is acceptable to all creeds and races. We continued to proclaim the wide availability of his great love for all mankind, and won no small number of converts to our faith.

Accompanying us on this journey was Titus, who since then has been my representative on many a hard mission, and whom I do not hesitate to call my son and brother in the faith. He was chosen to accompany Barnabas and me to Jerusalem because he was especially qualified to do so. A Greek by race, a Roman in name, a thorough Gentile who had never been circumcised nor embraced the religion of the Jews, he was a faithful worker and an earnest Christian. In short, he was a living proof that even a Gentile of the Gentiles might become a pillar of our church.

When I had last left Jerusalem, it had been with the consciousness of turning my back upon the old Jewish way of life, and facing toward a new and better way, a way that was thoroughly Christian, without adulteration of any other creed. This Christian way of life had led me among the Gentiles rather than among the Jews. Throughout my long missionary journey with Barnabas in Cyprus, Pamphylia, Pisidia and Lycaonia, it had been the Gentiles who had most readily listened to our preaching; the Jews had constantly pursued us, attempting to nullify our teaching, and at Lystra they had had me stoned, as they thought, to death.

This time, I was returning to Jerusalem to deal with a more subtle enemy than the open hatred of the Jews. This time, the enemy had struck from within our own communion. This time, the attackers of my work were those nominal Christians who had once been Pharisees and who even now were half Jew, half Christian, who wished to impose upon our faith the ceremonials and the dogma of Judaism.

Jerusalem was the natural seat of their activities. There, in the Holy City of the Jews, which was also the central shrine of Christendom, these Pharisaical theories had gained some foothold, even among the most exalted personages of our communion.

Having myself been a Pharisee, I could understand their arguments, and refute them all the better for this reason. I knew their way of thought, because I had once thought as they did. But in the fourteen years that had elapsed since my conversion, I had changed, and changed completely. They, too, had felt the impact of Truth as Jesus taught it, but they had not yet left the old way for the new. They hung, wavering, between the ancient and the contemporary, between Jewish ritual and Christian faith. Fellow-students of mine in the school of Gamaliel, they had not yet been fully graduated into the work of Christ.

They saw in me a person who wished to sever for all time the bonds that still held them, willing captives, to a teaching that had been outgrown. They feared the consequences if these bonds should be sharply cut by the sword of Truth. Their fear drove them at times to desperation.

When we arrived from Antioch, we were promptly received by the apostles and elders and leaders of the church. We told them joyfully of the growth of the church in Gentile lands: how God had smiled upon our work in many a town and city.

This was too much for the Pharisees and Judaizers who posed as Christians.

"Those converts," they declared, "should be circumcised, and commanded to keep the Law of Moses."

We, of course, opposed this with all our might until, in the hope of restoring harmony, the apostles and elders fixed a time for formal consideration of the matter.

In the meantime, Barnabas and I went privately to Peter and James, whom I knew, and to John, whose word carried great weight in our councils, to explain our case more fully. They heard us patiently, and were willing to agree that a division of labor might be made, so that they would continue with their work among the Hebrews, and we should go on with ours among the Gentiles.

They perceived the grace that had been given me in working among non-Jewish peoples, and gave to me and Barnabas their right hands as a pledge of fellowship.

This was the situation when the meeting or council formally assembled to consider this question.

After a general discussion and some sharp debate between ourselves and the Judaizing faction, Peter arose and made a memorable address.

"Brothers," he said, "you know that a good while ago God made a choice among us, that the Gentiles should hear the word of the gospel from my mouth, and believe."

This was a reference to Peter's experience in converting the Roman centurion Cornelius; to do this, he had gone into the centurion's house and eaten with him, in violation of all Hebrew law and custom. It had been revealed to Peter in a vision that this was permissible, and that there should be no dividing wall between Jews and Gentiles. The apostles and elders at Jerusalem had approved his action.

"God," continued Peter, "who knows all hearts, gave evidence of his favor toward the Gentiles, and bestowed

the Holy Spirit upon them, even as he did upon us. He
made no difference between us and them, and purified
their hearts by faith. Why therefore do you now tempt
God, so to speak, by putting a yoke upon the neck of the
disciples which neither our forefathers nor we ourselves
have been able to bear? For we believe that it is through
the grace of the Lord Jesus Christ that we, as well as
they, shall be saved."

Then Barnabas and I arose in turn and repeated our
accounts of the miracles and wonders that God had
wrought among the Gentiles at our hands. All were silent
as we spoke, and listened earnestly to our story.

James was the next to speak. The brother of Jesus was
known both to Jews and to Christians as "James the
Just," and great weight was given to his opinions. He
cited words of the prophet Amos to show that Christianity is the fulfillment of Judaism.

"My judgment is," concluded James, "that we should
not trouble those from among the Gentiles who have
turned to God, but that we should write to them, that
they abstain from things polluted by connection with
idolatry, and from fornication, and from meat killed by
strangling, and from blood."

This compromise solution relieved Gentile converts
from submitting to circumcision, yet obliged them to
observe certain others of the Jewish rites. It warned them
to be on their guard against eating meat or drinking
wine which might have been offered as sacrifices or libations to heathen gods. It urged them to maintain a
high standard of morals and purity. In short, it freed

them from the necessity of observing the ceremonials which were most burdensome, but at the same time kept some of the Jewish traditions in Christian worship.

This was what might have been expected of James. He was fond of tradition, and often subservient to it. He was on intimate terms with the Pharisaical faction. He had become a Christian only belatedly, after the crucifixion and resurrection of Jesus, but had soon been elevated to a position of formal pre-eminence. Even his personal appearance contributed to win him veneration: his features were austere, his hair and beard unshorn after the fashion of the Nazarites; he wore a simple, seamless garment of pure white, and his feet were bare. He looked like a prophet of olden times.

His proposal proved acceptable to the apostles and the elders, and was approved by the entire church. For myself, I accepted it as the best that could be obtained under the circumstances. I have never liked compromises, and this was a compromise. I should have liked to see a complete turning away from all Jewish tradition. But such a step was not yet feasible. James' proposal seemed to give promise of peace in the church, and that was essential. I raised no objection to the settlement that had been reached.

Our main point had been won. Circumcision was not to be required of Gentile converts to Christianity. Titus, for example, was not obliged to submit to the rite. His was a test case, to which we later had occasion to refer.

My conduct in preaching to the Gentiles had been

completely justified, and approved by the apostles. Our visit to Jerusalem had not been in vain, but had cleared up a confused and difficult situation.

Peter, James and John had expressed the wish that Barnabas and I, who had once brought relief to the needy Christians in Jerusalem, should continue to remember the righteous poor as we traveled, and to this I readily agreed. It has always been one of my happiest employments to share with the disciples at Jerusalem the bounty of our congregations in more prosperous Gentile lands.

These things being concluded, we returned to Antioch. With us went two of the leaders in the church at Jerusalem, Judas whose surname was Barsabas, and Silas. They were delegated by the apostles and the elders to accompany us as representatives of the church at Jerusalem, to bear witness to the understanding that had been reached there concerning the problem of the Gentiles.

We bore an official open letter to be proclaimed in the churches, as follows:

"The apostles and elders and disciples send greetings to the Gentile brothers in Antioch, Syria and Cilicia.

"Whereas we have heard that certain persons who went out from among us have troubled and disturbed you by saying, 'You must be circumcised and keep the law,' although we gave them no such instructions,

"Therefore it has seemed good to us, being assembled with one accord, to send chosen men to you with our beloved Barnabas and Paul, who have hazarded their lives for the name of our Lord Jesus Christ. We have therefore sent Judas and Silas, who will confirm these things by word of mouth.

"For it has seemed good to the Holy Spirit, and to us, to lay upon you no greater burden than these necessary things: that you abstain from meats offered to idols, from blood, from things strangled, and from fornication. Keep yourselves free from these things, and it shall be well with you. Farewell."

As soon as we reached Antioch, we called the entire church together and read the letter to them. When they had heard it, they rejoiced in the comfort that it brought them. And Judas and Silas, being men of vision, encouraged the brothers with their words and confirmed them in the faith. These two remained with us for a brief space of time, and received the blessing of our church. Then Judas returned to Jerusalem to the apostles, but Silas continued on at Antioch, and was shortly to become my companion on my second missionary journey.

We remained for some time in Antioch, however, and in the interval before we started on our journey occurred an incident which it pains me to recall. Yet I can at least rejoice that this quarrel, unhappy though it made me at the time, has since been replaced by a renewal of friendship and affection, and has left no trace of bitterness. My quarrel, strange as it may seem, was with Peter.

Peter, who had taken so firm a stand in favor of preaching to the Gentiles when I was at Jerusalem, and who was always ready to cite his own experience with Cor-

nelius as proof that the middle wall of partition between
Jews and Gentiles should be broken down, came to Antioch shortly afterwards, and was warmly welcomed by
the congregation.

He did not hesitate to enter into the houses of our
Gentile brothers and eat with them, and otherwise to
show his sympathy with the stand that Barnabas and I
had taken on the Gentiles' behalf.

He had not been long in Antioch, however, when new
visitors from Jerusalem arrived: men of the Pharisees'
faction in the church, friends of James. In spite of the
agreement that had been reached in the council at Jerusalem, some of these men had not yet lost their Pharisaical prejudices. They looked askance at Peter's frat-
ernizing with the Gentiles.

Peter became fearful of the reports that these Judaizers
might carry back to the apostles and elders in Jerusalem.
His whole attitude and manner of conduct changed. He
excused himself from associating with the Gentiles, and
began to hold himself entirely separate and aloof from
them.

It made me sad to observe this, but it seemed unwise
at first to remark upon it. However, I soon discovered
that Barnabas and others were being misled, and that
many were concealing their real opinions and being in-
timidated.

As soon as I saw that they were not walking uprightly
according to Truth, I determined to withstand Peter in
the presence of them all, because he was to blame for
this.

"If you, being a Jew," said I to Peter, confronting him publicly in the congregation, "live after the fashion of the Gentiles, and not as a Jew, why do you compel the Gentiles to live like Jews? You and I, who are Jews by birth, and not Gentiles, know that a man cannot be saved by obedience to the Jewish law, but only by faith in Jesus Christ."

And I reasoned with him publicly to show him the error of his ways. He stood there before me, his powerful, broad shoulders slightly bent as if to bear the lash of my rebuke, his strong, honest face, framed in curly beard, revealing his dismay at what I said.

Ah, Peter, perhaps I was hasty. You have always been a man of quick impulses, but most of those impulses have been good. You changed often, but you always changed more readily from evil to good than from good to evil.

On that occasion, you bore me no bitterness for my scolding. I must have looked strange to you as I stood there storming at you, my face flushed, my eyes flashing, my head reaching hardly to your armpits, like a terrier barking at a mastiff.

You bore me no bitterness for my scolding. Since then, you have called me your beloved brother. And now, it seems we may at any moment share the same fate—if you have not already suffered martyrdom without my hearing of it, at the hands of my jailer, Nero. Peter, my beloved Peter, I have always loved you. Think not ill of me because once, twenty long years ago, I raged at you in Antioch. I felt then that I was in the right. But is it ever right for brothers to quarrel?

*   *   *

The remainder of this sojourn at Antioch was clouded not only by this disagreement with Peter, but by other events.

Disturbing reports came to me of that Thekla who had thrust herself upon me at Iconium. The story was told that after Barnabas and I had left that city, she had been taken for a witch, and the governor had condemned her to be burned. But when they had kindled the fire under her, the heavens opened and poured down water that put the fire out, and she was saved. It was said that she was on her way to Antioch to seek me out again.

Indeed she did appear in Antioch, and I arranged that she should live with a widow of our congregation, for she was much disturbed, and seemed at times not in the full possession of her senses.

Springing chiefly from her wild imaginings, strange tales were spread about her: how she had been condemned to be thrown to wild beasts, and how, when this sentence was carried out, the beasts, including lions and bears and a lioness, and bulls, and fierce water creatures, had all refused to attack her, and had on the contrary shielded her from harm.

One could not know when she spoke of things which actually had happened, and when she spoke of figments of her fancy. Yet she was fair, and good to all, and many felt that she was in close communion with the Holy

Spirit. She strove constantly to be with me, but I contrived that she should be kept in calm security away from throngs, and in the care of kindly women.

I did not let her know when I left Antioch, but in time she learned that I had gone, and followed me.

*   *   *

One other last unhappy event transpired before I started on my journey. It was another quarrel, this time with Barnabas.

He had brought back with him, from our last visit to Jerusalem, his young kinsman Mark, who had so unceremoniously left us when we reached Perga on our former journey.

Now I had received inspiration to proceed on another mission, and I wished Barnabas for a companion.

"Let us go again and visit our brothers," I said to him, "in every city where we have preached the word of the Lord, and see how they do."

Barnabas was eager to join me. But he made a proposal I could not approve.

"We will take Mark with us," said he. "The lad is dear to me, and he longs to travel in the service of the Master."

"He may indeed be dear to you," I said, "but it seems not good to me to carry with us one who so lightly departed from us in Pamphylia, and went not with us to the work."

Then Barnabas made many excuses for his kinsman, how that he was then young, and devoted to his mother at Jerusalem, whom he wished to see; that he was now more mature, had seen the error of his way, and would not again abandon us in time of need.

Yet all this sounded not well in my ears. I had seen no proof that the lad had changed.

"On such a journey as we are to make," I told him, "there is no place for useless baggage."

"Dare you call my kinsman useless baggage?" cried Barnabas. "I'll have a retraction from you, or we will not travel with you."

"You'll have no apology from me," I shouted. "Go, take your timid little kinsman and travel where you will."

It was all so petty, so unnecessary. I am not proud of my part in it. I do not think that Barnabas was, after the quarrel was over, nor even Mark himself.

But pride and stubbornness had parted us.

Barnabas took Mark, and sailed again for Cyprus.

I chose Silas for my partner. The church gave us its blessing, and we departed from Antioch, not to Cyprus, but by land through Syria to my native Cilicia. It seemed good to me to be again on the road. The traveler's way has ever been my way.

Eight

I T WAS on this second journey that I carried the
glad tidings of Christ Jesus from Asia into Europe. There were already Christian communities in the
principal cities of Greece, but I was the first to under-
take a systematic visit of the churches there.

Since then the growth of our communion in the Greek
and Roman lands has been sound and rapid. The seed I
sowed has brought forth abundantly.

When I left Antioch with Silas, we had no intention
of traveling so far afield. My original intention, as I had
told Barnabas, was merely to revisit the churches we had
seen or founded on our first journey. But God, who gov-
erns the affairs of men, led me even to another conti-
nent in the way that I shall explain.

After brief sojourns in several towns of Syria, we
crossed the northern mountains by the pass known as
the Syrian Gates into Cilicia, and came to my native

city of Tarsus. Here the church where I had labored for several years was now taking firm hold, the influence of its teachings being felt in the life of many of the citizens, including friends of my childhood and youth.

Cheered by this evidence of fruitage, we pressed on across the high range of Taurus by the pass of the Cilician Gates, up rocky gorges and through narrow defiles, beside foaming mountain torrents, and finally down again from the mountain heights to the lofty plain of Lycaonia. The hard journey took four days, and we were often in peril of floods and of robbers, but God spared us and brought us safely through.

First of my former haunts to be revisited was Derbe, where we were well received by the congregation, who made many inquiries concerning Barnabas, and greeted no less warmly my new companion, Silas.

Then to Lystra, where I had been worshiped and then stoned. And here was my beloved Timothy, who in my absence had grown in virtue and in understanding, spiritually nurtured by his mother Eunice and his grandmother Lois.

The temple of Jupiter, whose priest had come to sacrifice to Barnabas and me, as to Jupiter and Mercury, still drew its votaries, and the idolatrous aspect of the city had hardly altered. But one knew that within the hearts of some of its people a new day was dawning and a truer view of God was being gained.

So good were the reports of Timothy's growth and work, his knowledge of the Scriptures and his unfeigned faith, that I determined to take him with me on my journey. There were reasons, even in addition to his character, that led me to this decision.

The fact that his mother was a Jewess, while his father was a Greek, especially fitted him for our mission. Silas and I were carrying with us, and reading to the churches, the decree adopted at the council in Jerusalem governing the relations between the Jews and the Gentiles of our communion. Having both Greek and Jewish blood, Timothy by very reason of his birth seemed to represent the union of these two elements in our congregations, which we hoped to reconcile with one another.

But Timothy, whose mother was a Jewess, had never been circumcised because the household had been long since converted to our Christian faith, and Timothy thought of himself as neither Jew nor Greek, but as a Christian.

The letter which Silas and I brought from Jerusalem to the churches expressly indicated that converts to our faith need not undergo circumcision. Yet I thought it wise to circumcise Timothy when I took him with me on my journey.

I have been criticized for this, and think it well to explain my action. I acted not from any belief in the rite of circumcision. I, Paul, who have throughout my ministry sought to free our Christian faith from Jewish ceremonial and tradition, cannot be thought to have acted in this case from any conviction that circumcision was necessary to a Christian. In Christ Jesus neither circumcision nor uncircumcision is of any importance; but only faith working through Love, which makes each of us a new creature.

Why, then, did I circumcise Timothy? Only because it seemed expedient to meet the objections that would have arisen otherwise, and in order that our ministry might be more fully accomplished.

If I had taken with me on my journey an uncircumcised person of Gentile blood, I would have shut myself off entirely from the Jewish world, and even from many Jews who had become Christians. If the Jews in this very town of Lystra, and in Iconium, had only a short time before tried to stone me to death, who was born a Jew and circumcised only eight days later, what would they not have done to Timothy, had I taken him, uncircumcised, for a companion?

Moreover, there were still in our communion many of Jewish birth who clung to the old traditions and superstitions. They had not accepted—many of them had not yet heard—the decisions of the council at Jerusalem which Silas and I were now coming to communicate to them. Had they heard that we were bringing with us an uncircumcised Gentile—and this is the rumor that would have gone before us—they would not even have met with us to hear us read and explain the letter from the council.

An earnest Jew felt himself defiled by eating with an uncircumcised person. How could we ever have entered into terms of friendship with Jews or Jewish converts to our faith under such conditions?

Some have said that I was inconsistent in that I cir

cumcised Timothy, while at Jerusalem I had opposed the circumcision of Titus and other Gentiles. The two cases were not parallel. Titus was a Gentile, without a trace of Jewish blood. The question at Jerusalem was whether he, and Gentiles like him, should be compelled to submit to circumcision in order to be accepted as Christians.

In the case of Timothy, there was no question of compulsion. The issue here was merely whether it would not be expedient for Timothy, whose mother was a Jewess, to be circumcised by his own consent in order to allay the fears and suspicions of the Jews and our Jewish converts as he went with me among them. Had this not been done, they never would have received us, nor could they have been liberated from their bondage.

These were the reasons that led me to circumcise Timothy, even though I bore a letter from Jerusalem saying that Gentiles need not be circumcised to enter our communion. After the rite was performed, he proceeded with me and Silas to Iconium and beyond.

We now left the route of my former journey, and traveled into Phrygia and Galatia. In these wild and remote regions, peopled by the lovable but fickle Gauls, I suffered from a sickness that came upon me. But even as I lay ill, I spread the Word of God among the natives, with good results.

These people did not think the less of me because I was ill; they did not despise me nor reject my teachings because, although I spoke words of divine import, I was subject to human frailty. On the contrary, they received me warmly, as if I had been an angel of God, or even Christ Jesus himself.

So deeply attached were they to me that they would have plucked out their own eyes and given them to me, if that would have served any useful purpose. I have never forgotten their loving-kindness, to which I have paid tribute in a letter that I wrote to them long since from Rome.*

By the time we were ready to leave this region, churches had been planted in various towns and cities, and a blow dealt to the shameful worship of the heathen goddess Cybele at Pessinus.

My health and strength being now restored, we pressed on westwards to the sea, descending to the shores of the Aegean, to the region known as the Troad, site of the historic city of Troy. Here, where one could look out across the water to islands that seemed to float upon the surface of the sea, and even beyond to the lofty summit of Mt. Athos on the European shore, we might have halted, or taken ship home to Antioch.

But a vision came to me in the night, a vision that was to lead me to new fields of work and adventure. I saw standing before me, clear as day, a man of Macedonia, from the land westward beyond the sea.

"Come over into Macedonia," said he, "and help us."

For such a revelation, there could be no other explanation than that God had called me to preach the good news to the Macedonians. I hastened to do his bid-

* The Epistle to the Galatians, 4.13-15.

ding. A ship was found, ready to make the western voyage. We went aboard, and shortly sailed.

With me went not only Silas and Timothy, but a new addition to our little band of missionaries. This was Luke, a physician of great kindness, who has since accompanied me over many a mile by land and sea.

A keen observer, a man of vision, he has made a practice of noting down the events and sequence of our travels, and thus compiled a journal of our wanderings.* Likewise, he has interviewed all those at Jerusalem and elsewhere who knew our Lord, and written a record of the days of Jesus' ministry.†

The four of us set sail for Macedonia. It was a move of great consequence for the Western world. For as a result of this and later voyages, Truth now flourishes in many a city of Europe, which once was dark in superstition.

With a fair wind behind us, we were soon past the islands of Tenedos and Imbros, and anchored for the night in the shelter of the lofty mountain-isle of Samothrace. Then, the favorable wind continuing, we crossed in another day to Neapolis, in Macedonia, where we first set foot on European soil. Neapolis is the port for Philippi, ten miles distant. To that important and historic city we at once proceeded. It was there that our European ministry properly began.

* The Acts of the Apostles.
† The Gospel According to St. Luke.

Nine

M<small>ANY</small> adventures befell us at Philippi, first Macedonian city where we preached the joyful tidings.

This was a thoroughly Roman community. It was not a place of much commerce, but primarily a garrison town, well furnished with imperial troops.

There were few Jews here, not enough to justify the maintaining of a synagogue. This being the case, the small Jewish population made a practice of meeting on the Sabbath in an outdoor place of prayer, or propseucha, outside the city wall on the bank of the river Gaggitas.

On the first Sabbath that we spent in the city, we visited this congregation, which consisted almost entirely of women, many of whom were natives of other places, but had been drawn to Philippi for one reason or another.

Among the converts or proselytes to Judaism who gathered here, an outstanding one was Lydia, a woman from the city of Thyatira, in Asia, who was a seller of the purple dye for which her native city was famous.

As we in turn addressed the gathering, Lydia drank in our words. The Lord opened her heart to the things that I was led to say. She became an earnest convert to our cause, and she and her whole household were baptized. Being a kind-hearted woman, given to hospitality, she invited us to make her home our domicile as long as we were in Philippi.

"If you have found me to be faithful to the Lord," said Lydia to us, "come and stay at my house."

She pleaded with us so earnestly that we felt constrained to go and live there.

Thus, our first experience on European soil was one of loving-kindness and hospitality. Would that such experiences might have continued! But the contrary was to be our lot, and soon.

One day, as we went from Lydia's house to the place of prayer, we were met by a girl slave who was supposed to be endowed with the power of divination. She made much money by telling fortunes, and her earnings went to several persons who owned her in common. They sent her out into the streets each day to ply her trade, and then divided her fees among them.

This poor creature was not entirely unreceptive to the Truth we taught. Some faint inkling of its meaning seems to have penetrated her understanding as we preached, and she attached herself to us, to our embar-

rassment. As we went about our business, she would
follow us, crying out and performing strange antics.

"These men," she would shout, "are the servants of
the most high God. They are showing us the way to
salvation!"

This attracted throngs of idlers and curious persons.
We tried to dissuade the girl from following us, but she
continued to do so, as if in a trance. It was easy to see
that she acted under the influence of some strange ob-
session. Her words bore witness to Truth, but her manner and actions were those of one demented. After many
days of this, during which we tolerated her troublesome
interference, I determined to put an end to it.

One day, when she had been more than usually an-
noying, I turned on her and rebuked the unruly spirit
that seemed to have taken possession of her.

"In the name of Jesus the Christ," said I, addressing
the evil that was governing her actions, "I command
you to come out of her."

Immediately she was freed from her delusion and became a normal, reasonable person. Naturally, she lost at
this same instant any desire or ability to carry on her
questionable trade of fortune-telling.

When her owners saw that they were deprived of the
illegitimate income the maid had brought them, they
were furious. They lay in wait for me and Silas and when
they saw a chance they seized us and dragged us, pro-
testing in the midst of a curious crowd, to the public
square and into the place where the magistrates, or prae-

tors, were holding court. As soon as the magistrates were ready to hear them, they made charges against us.

"These men," they told the court, "are Jews. They are stirring up trouble in our city by teaching customs which we, as Romans, are not legally permitted to accept nor observe."

And they went on at great length, accusing us of all sorts of crimes and misdemeanors, and of treason against the Roman authorities.

Jews were not welcome in Philippi, and were always under suspicion of plotting against their Roman rulers. This was a thoroughly Roman garrison town, and the authorities were inclined to be very strict with anything that had even a taint of disloyalty to the Roman rule. The Jews had recently been expelled from Rome by the emperor Claudius.

A mob of excited Philippians had followed us to be present at our trial. They kept up an outcry against us, urging the magistrates to deal with us harshly. This influenced the court. The judges decreed that we should be flogged and imprisoned.

No time was lost in carrying out their sentence. Silas and I were stripped of our clothes and cruelly beaten, then hurried off to jail. The jailer was given special orders to see that we were safely locked up, and in compliance with this command we were cast into an inner cell of the prison, and our feet made fast in stocks.

Only a few hours earlier, we had been free men, going about our divinely appointed task in the open air and sunlight of the city, accompanied by friends and engaged in winning new followers to the cause of Christ.

Now we were hidden away in prison slime and darkness, all but naked, the blood still flowing from our lacerated backs and shoulders, our limbs strained and tortured in the vise-like grip of the stocks. Our mission to Macedonia, that had begun so brightly with the conversion and loving hospitality of Lydia, now seemed doomed to failure.

But I had already learned a sure release from hardship, despair and suffering. This was not my first imprisonment, nor my first flogging. Experience had already shown me that what seemed the darkest hour was often but the prelude to a bright tomorrow.

"Silas," said I, "let us pray."

We both turned for solace to God, in whose service we had learned to glory. As we prayed we were freed from pain and discouragement and fear. The dark forebodings that had settled down upon us were dispelled. We gained again the courage and the joy that we had had before our arrest and punishment.

"At least we can rejoice," thought I, "that the slave girl is freed from her delusion, and no longer preying upon good people in this city, for the profit of her wicked owners."

As my spirits mounted, I turned to my companion with a new proposal.

"Let us sing," said I to Silas, "one of the psalms we used to sing with our brothers at Antioch."

Our voices may have quavered in the opening bars, but soon we were immersed in the beauty of the words of praise that had arisen from many a Christian heart in all the cities we had visited. Words of hope and salvation; words of loving-kindness and compassion. Words that swept through the dark corridors of the prison at the midnight hour and awakened our fellow-prisoners to such thoughts as they had never had before, nor ever hoped to hear expressed in prison cells at Philippi.

"O give thanks to the Lord," we sang, "for he is good;
    For his mercy endures forever.
    Such as sit in darkness and in the shadow of death,
    Being bound in affliction and iron;
    He brings them out of darkness and the shadow of
        death,
    And breaks their bonds asunder." *

Except for our words, echoing through the stone-walled passages of the prison, not a sound was to be heard. Yet we knew that the other inmates were awake. We felt them listening in the darkness. Above us, below us, all around us, were wondering men, marveling that those cast into prison bloody and suffering, as we had been, should sing—and what a song!

"He sent his word and healed them,
    And delivered them from their destructions.
    O that men would praise the Lord for his goodness,
    And for his wonderful works to the children of men!"

From a dungeon deep below us arose a wavering voice, chanting with us the wondrous, familiar words of the

* Psalm 107.

age-old psalm. Then another, from a distant cell along
the corridor. Soon a choir of oddly assorted voices was
singing the strangest anthem that the world had ever
known. Their voices gained strength as the hymn proceeded, and soon the massive building seemed to vibrate
with the rising tide of sound.

"For he has broken the gates of brass," we thundered,
"And cut the bars of iron asunder."

At that instant, a strange thing happened. The very
foundations of the building shifted, as if moved from
their rocky moorings by the torrent of our song. The
gates and doors swung open, and chains and fetters clat-
tered on the stony floors. The stocks that held our feet
sprang open wide. It was an earthquake.

Yet no man stirred. There was no rush for freedom,
no stampede through the barriers. Each sat where he was,
knowing that he was free, rejoicing in his deliverance,
singing as if he could not sing loudly enough to voice the
happiness that was in his heart. I could not see the
singers, but I knew that in each face there shone a light
such as had never illumined it before. The song continued:

"They cried to the Lord in their trouble,
 And he delivered them out of their distresses,
 And he led them forth by the right way."

As our hymn drew to a close, an eerie light began to
permeate the place. I saw the warden of the prison, awakened from his slumbers, wild-eyed with fear and despera-

tion, come stumbling through an open door. He gazed uncomprehendingly at the gates ajar, the broken chains and fetters. Terror overcame him as he realized that he would be put to death if his prisoners had escaped. He drew his sword and was about to plunge it into his breast when I called out to him:

"Do yourself no harm, for we are all here."

Surprise and amazement overwhelmed him. His sword clanged on the stony floor, as he dropped it where he stood.

"Lights! Lights!" he shouted. "Bring lights at once!"

Torches flared along the passageways as attendants came running.

The keeper rushed into our cell. When he saw us there, unshackled and unharmed, he all but collapsed. Trembling, he threw himself at our feet.

"Sirs," he cried, "what must I do to be saved?"

"Believe on the Lord Jesus Christ," said I, "and you shall be saved, and all your household."

A great peace descended upon us all. The jailer felt our calm, and regained his poise. Then he arose and led us to his house, which adjoined the prison. He called his family and servants together to minister to our needs. They washed our wounds and clothed us in fresh linen, and gave us food, and we meanwhile preached the word of God to them.

And all the jailer's household believed, and were baptized straightway.

*   *   *

The story of our miraculous deliverance from prison was carried directly to the magistrates who had caused us to be flogged and imprisoned. They were much perturbed, and determined that Silas and I should be sent away as promptly as possible. If prisons would not hold us, they reasoned, they could not control us, and they feared to put to death anyone with such miraculous powers.

They sent word by the police early in the morning that we were to be released at once. Our kindly host, the keeper of the prison, was overjoyed to get this news, and hastened to tell us of it.

"The magistrates have sent to let you go. Now you may depart, and go your way in peace."

But I chose not to be smuggled out of the city in any such fashion, after having undergone indignity and suffering there, all unjustly. I confronted the police officers, or lictors, with these facts.

"The magistrates," I said, "have flogged us publicly without a trial, and have cast us into prison. But we are Roman citizens, to whom such things cannot legally be done. Now do they think they can hurry us out of the city in secret and cover up their mistake? By no means. Let them come themselves and release us in due and proper form."

The lictors carried my message to the praetors, who were much disturbed when they heard that we were Roman citizens. They feared the discipline they might be subjected to if their error became known. They knew very well that they had exceeded their authority.

We had had no proper trial. In permitting us to be scourged publicly, the magistrates had allowed the dignity of Roman citizens to be assailed. This was especially reprehensible in a Roman garrison town such as Philippi, where the prestige of Rome was zealously maintained.

The magistrates came immediately to the prison, formally released us, and pleaded with us to leave the city. They felt that our continued presence there would keep alive the memory of their fault. Summary punishment might be forthcoming from Rome if word of this reached the capital, as it was almost certain to do.

We made no promises, but went again to the hospitable house of Lydia, where we were joyously reunited with our friends. We bore witness to them of the protecting love of God, which we had so abundantly experienced, and they joined with us in giving thanks for our deliverance.

Then, with the church strengthened and established in the city, Silas and I took our leave of them and proceeded on our journey. Timothy and Luke remained behind, further to comfort and encourage them.

Ten

—

PRESSING eastward across Macedonia, we came to Thessalonica.* This was a very different city from Philippi. It was not a Roman garrison town, but a great trading metropolis and seaport. Unlike Philippi, it had a large Jewish population.

We began our ministry, as usual, by taking part in the services of the synagogue. For three successive Sabbaths, I went in and reasoned with them out of the Scriptures, showing them that Jesus, who had suffered and risen from the dead, was indeed the Christ.

Some of the Jews believed, and consorted with me and Silas; but a much greater number of Gentiles rallied to our cause. Here, as elsewhere, the Greeks showed themselves more receptive to our teaching than the Jews. Also, as elsewhere, many women joined our congregation, including some of the chief women of the city.

* Modern Salonika

But the Jews who would not receive our teaching grew jealous of our successes. They were envious of the numbers that flocked to our communion. Some of their leaders, as at Iconium and Lystra, enlisted a gang of lewd fellows of the baser sort, and set the city in an uproar, accusing us of disturbing the peace.

Silas and I were staying in the house of one of the disciples named Jason, a true and loyal man who had welcomed us and bade us make his home our own.

One day when we were absent, the gang of ruffians whom the Jews had organized descended upon Jason's house in force, shouting and demanding that we be surrendered to the people. When they found that we were not there, they seized Jason and others of the disciples who happened to be with him at the time, and rushed them off to the civil authorities. Thessalonica was a free city of the empire, and had its own governing board or court of seven officials, known as politarchs.

Pulling and hauling Jason and his companions before the court as it was sitting, these noisy Jews made a great outcry.

"Those troublesome fellows who have turned the world upside down have now come here to Thessalonica," they cried, "and this man Jason has received them into his house. All of them are violating the decrees of Caesar, for they go about saying that there is another king, one Jesus!"

The judges and the people who stood about were much troubled when they heard these things.

But Jason and his friends made a patient and convincing plea on my behalf and Silas', declaring that we meant no harm to the city or its rulers, but were honest men of sober life, who had never taken part in any insurrection, nor would lend our influence to any disorder whatsoever.

Finally the court decreed that we should be permitted to remain in the city on sufferance, providing Jason and one of his companions would post a money bond as security for our good conduct. This was done, the tumult subsided, and Jason returned to his house with his friends.

When we came home to Jason's house at the close of the day, we heard what had transpired in our absence. It distressed me greatly that Jason or any other of the brothers should have been put to any expense on our account.

During the weeks that we had been in Thessalonica, I had taken special care to relieve our congregation there of any financial burden arising from our visit. I had searched out an opportunity to make use of my own handicraft, and had given such time as I could spare to my old trade of tent-making.

Again I saw how wise my father had been in insisting that I should learn a trade. What I could earn was sufficient to meet my simple needs, and I was dependent upon no man. No one could say that my presence was burdensome to the church. How true is the old Jewish maxim:

"He that has a trade in his hand, to what can he be likened? He is like a vineyard that is fenced."

Yet in spite of my care for this matter, Jason had been obliged to furnish bond for me. My continued presence in the city would have caused him and his fellow Christians embarrassment and expense.

Silas and I were agreed that such a situation would be unbearable. That very night we took our leave of the disciples, and they saw us on our way toward our next stopping-place, Beroea.

Here, as in Thessalonica, there was a Jewish community. We found them of a more noble sort than the Jews of Thessalonica, who had treated us so shamefully. They received our teaching with open minds, and searched the Scriptures daily to confirm our doctrines. Many of these Jews believed, and so did many Greeks, both men and women.

We might have stayed indefinitely in Beroea, and been welcome there, had not news of our preaching been sent to the malicious Jews of Thessalonica. Word of our activities was not long in reaching them, and they hastened to make the sixty-mile journey to Beroea to thwart and persecute us.

They began to organize just such a demonstration as they had made against us in their own city. But knowledge of their plot came to me in time so that I could withdraw and spare the church in Beroea the same embarrassment that Jason and the others had felt in Thessalonica.

I went down to the sea and took ship for Athens. But Silas and Timothy, who had meanwhile rejoined us, stayed behind at Beroea to help and encourage the church. Some of the disciples from Beroea went with me on my journey southward.

And so I left Macedonia, after my first visit there. The roots of the church had for the first time been firmly planted on European shores. I had suffered flogging, imprisonment, and almost constant persecution, but God's work had been done and there had been rich fruitage.

In Philippi I had been faced with pagan hatred and superstition, but the fortune-telling slave girl had been delivered from her delusion and a blow dealt against ignorance and cupidity. I had, all unjustly, felt the Roman lash and suffered imprisonment, but I had been divinely delivered, my Roman rights had at last been recognized, and even my jailer had become a member of the church.

In Thessalonica and Beroea, I had faced more familiar enemies: Jewish hatred and envy; but I had been delivered from them by the faithfulness of friends and the mercy of God.

Now, as I took ship in the very shadow of the Mount Olympus which the Greeks call the home of their gods, I was again a fugitive, but not disheartened. I knew that even the jealousy of the Jews must yield in time to the love of Christ.

As for those superstitions which seemed to have their chief monument in the snow-crowned peak that rose behind us as we put to sea, I knew that they, too, must go down before the onward march of Truth.

We set our course for Athens, the very source and

origin of that Godless way of life which it was my mission to cast down, and rear upon its ruins a new and higher faith.

*   *   *

Sailing southward through beauteous blue waters, we swung around the southernmost promontory of Attica and headed west and north in the Saronic Gulf. We had not gone far in this direction when we caught our first indication of where Athens lay.

As we stood on deck, drinking in the wonders of sea and land and sky, a flash of reflected sunlight reached our eyes. It came from the polished armor of the gigantic statue of Minerva that stood atop the Athenian citadel.

That flash had something in it of defiance. It was as if the fabled goddess, guardian of the city, had sensed our coming, and brandished her spear and shield to warn us off. One might have thought the heathen gods felt the approach of their impending doom, and sought to frighten from their shores the messengers who brought Truth into their very stronghold.

Undismayed by Minerva's threatening flashes, we bore straight onward and, gliding smoothly through the harbor's entrance, dropped anchor at Piraeus, port of Athens.

Also at anchor, or moored at docks, were ships of all descriptions, from little fishing boats which brought their daily catch to market here, to tall grain-ships from Alexandria and the Black Sea. The landing-places that

lined the harbor were partly covered with porticoes; in
the shade lounged sea-faring men from every known
port. In squalid huts and houses that ran almost to the
water's edge lived the motley population of this teeming
Athenian suburb.

A gloomy fortress overhung the harbor. Warehouses
for storing grain were dotted here and there beside the
landing-places. There were amphitheaters where the
sailors gathered to applaud the bawdy comedies of Me-
nander. Here, too, were temples to heathen gods and
goddesses, falsely supposed to govern the destinies of
men. They included an altar inscribed—in depths of pit-
iable ignorance—"TO AN UNKNOWN GOD."

We went ashore and began the journey on foot from
the port to Athens. The straight road we followed had
on either side a ruined wall of vast proportions. These
famous long walls, which had served to protect the com-
munication of the city with its seaport, were once sixty
feet in height, but had now dwindled away, in places,
to almost nothing. Much of the hewn stone they contained had been hauled away to build other structures.

At the end of this five-mile avenue, we entered the
city by the Peiraic gate. Here was Athens, vaunted home
of art and learning, fountainhead of Hellenic culture.
As we walked through its colonnaded streets, I was both
smitten with its beauty and saddened by its depths of
superstition.

Here was a city wholly given to idolatry. At almost
every step, one found new evidence of its people's genius

for worshiping gods wrought with human hands. Here was an image of Neptune, god of the sea, hurling his trident. Then a temple of Ceres, goddess of the harvest. There were sculptured figures of Minerva, Jupiter, Apollo, Mercury and the Muses. Close at hand stood a shrine to Bacchus, god of wine.

We came to the Agora, an open square which was the meeting-place of the Athenians, where they love to stroll in the sunshine, conversing, disputing, gossiping. Streams of people were passing by on every sort of errand, and under the painted and sculptured porticoes at the sides were little knots of men, exchanging their views on topics of the day. The Athenians love to talk.

Here were statues of the famous men of Athens: Solon the lawgiver, Demosthenes the orator; and mingled with these actual personages of the past were representations of mythical heroes: of Hercules and Theseus. Thus do the Athenians mingle the mortal with the divine, making gods of men and men of gods.

Here were shrines to Juno, to Vesta, to every pagan god and goddess. As if this were not enough, altars were erected to abstract qualities, such as Fame, and Modesty, and Persuasion, and Pity, and Energy; even to Disdain, and to Immodesty. These Athenians, it appeared, would worship anything to which a name or a form could be given, and many things which defied representation even by their most skillful sculptors.

These sights weighed heavily upon me, as I wandered alone through the city. Those who had come with me

from Beroea I had sent immediately back to Macedonia, to tell Silas and Timothy, who had stayed behind,
to hasten to me. They were long in coming, and I was
left to myself in this strange, heathen capital.

The Jews had a synagogue in Athens, and according
to my custom I went there and voiced Truth to them.
Not unmindful of my mission to the Gentiles, I also
mingled with the groups of talkers in the Agora, and
heard their views.

Here in this wilderness of conflicting philosophics and
creeds, I found the chief among the disputants to belong
to two schools or sects, the Epicureans and the Stoics.
These latter were not unfamiliar to me, as I had talked
with them in my native city, Tarsus, where they were
strongly established.

The Stoics took their name from the Stoa Poecile, or
Painted Cloister, in the Agora at Athens, where they
were accustomed to gather. Theirs was a stern, unyield-
ing way of thought; a proud, selfish, hard and fatalistic
system of philosophy. As I talked to them of the Christ,
they listened patiently, but without comprehension.
God's love for man was not within the limits of their
reasoning.

The Epicureans were no nearer than the Stoics to
Truth. Seeking only pleasure, and given to the gratifica-
tion of the senses, they could not understand that true
contentment is to be found not in the flesh, but in Spirit.
When I talked to them of Jesus and the resurrection,
they turned away unmoved, to the philosophic delights

of that garden which their founder, Epicurus, had bequeathed to them, and where they sought to perpetuate his teaching.

Still, my discussions with these pagan thinkers left some slight imprint on their consciousness. They scoffed, but they were curious.

"What has this babbler to say?" asked some.

"He seems to be a preacher of strange gods," said others.

Their natural curiosity led them, in spite of scoffing, to listen to me and discuss my sayings. For it was the way of the Athenians, and of strangers who came to live in their city, to spend all their time in doing nothing else but listening to or telling of some new, strange fact or theory.

After some days had passed in reasoning with them, they so far took notice of my teaching as to lead me up Mars' Hill, to the Court of Areopagus, to expound my philosophy, as they called it.

"May we hear what is this new doctrine, that you teach?" they asked. "For you bring certain strange things to our ears. We would like to know what these things mean."

There, in the awesome presence of their highest court, and in surroundings of great solemnity, I preached to them of Jesus and the resurrection.

The place where I stood was a small semicircle hewn from the rock near the crest of the hill. The judges were seated on a crescent-shaped bench of stone; at either end

of the crescent was a stone platform, and on these, when
trials were in progress, the accuser and the accused took
their places. I was not on trial, and therefore stood before
the judges, who listened with interest and curiosity to
what I had to say.

As I looked about me, I was again struck with the evidence of idolatry that stood forth on every hand. Above
us rose a temple to Mars, god of war, whose name was
given to this hill.

Not far away was the cavern of the Furies, mythical
creatures who pursued their victims with relentless fierce-
ness. How different from the God of Love that I had
come to tell them of!

Across a little valley to my right rose the Acropolis,
central shrine of all this artificial world, embellished with
temples and statues of every god and mythical creature
that the fertile imagination of the Athenians had been
able to devise. The intricate sculptures, the symmetrical
outlines of the temple columns and entablatures, shone
sharply through the clear air of a sunny afternoon, and
all the grace and charm of heathen culture seemed to
dispute the very words I uttereed.

Above the highest temple roof rose the gigantic statue
of Minerva, the glint of whose armor I had seen from
far out at sea. Again the goddess seemed to shake her
gleaming spear and shield to threaten me for raising
my voice against their brilliant parody of godliness.

"Men of Athens," said I, "I perceive that in every
respect you are remarkably religious. For as I passed

through your city, and beheld the objects of your worship, I found an altar with this inscription: TO AN UNKNOWN GOD. This God, therefore, whom you worship without knowing him, I now proclaim to you.

"God who made the world and all things therein, who is Lord of heaven and earth, dwells not in temples made with hands, neither is he served by men's hands, as though he needed anything. For he gives to all men life, and breath, and all things."

A murmur of dissent ran through the group of philosophers who had escorted me up the steps to where the court was sitting. One of the judges on the bench shifted his position. Tactful as I had tried to be, I found they did not relish being told that all their artful image-making and formal worship was mere vanity.

"This God," I continued, "has made all nations of one blood to dwell on all the face of the earth, and has fixed the times and boundaries of their habitations; that they should seek the Lord, if perhaps they might grope after him, and find him. Yet he is not far from every one of us.

"For in him we live, and move, and have our being. As certain of your own poets (for example, Aratus, who like myself was a native of Cilicia) have said, 'For we are also his offspring.'

"Since, then, we are the offspring of God, we ought not to think that God is like gold, or silver, or stone, sculptured by the art and skill of man."

Here there was more murmuring among the audience and the judges, and I saw more than one eye being turned toward the rich sculptures and gilded statues on the Acropolis, in admiration of their beauty and in keen displeasure with my words. But I appeared not to notice this, and went on with what I had to say.

"God," I told them, "has overlooked this ignorance in the past, but he now commands all men everywhere to repent, for he has appointed a day on which he will judge the world in righteousness by that man whom he has appointed for this work; and this fact he has proved to all by raising that man from the dead."

With this challenging statement I closed my discourse. There was no applause. The judges smiled or exchanged remarks among themselves, and indicated that they would proceed with the business of the day. Some of the audience laughed softly and made jokes about my statement that God had raised a man from the dead. One or two jeered audibly.

But a few of those with whom I had talked in the market-place gathered around me.

"We will hear you again on this subject," they said.

Later I learned that my appearance before the court had not been so unproductive as it seemed. One of the judges, a prominent Athenian named Dionysius, had been persuaded of the truth of what I had said. He became a member of our communion; also a woman named Damaris, and others.

The seed had been sown in the very hothouse of paganism. There it has had to fight its way up through the tangled undergrowth of sensualism and idolatry. Indifference and skepticism have hindered its growth. Yet it is there, and will bring forth fruit in its time. A faltering faith in heathen gods must give way at last to the worship of the God not made with hands.

Eleven

—

As ATHENS appeared to be an unpromising field of work, I did not tarry there. I was not stoned, nor imprisoned, nor otherwise persecuted. But the cold intellectualism, the polite indifference, the scoffing wit, of its inhabitants were a more serious barrier to Truth than the open indignity and suffering which were my lot in other cities.

Corinth, metropolis of the province of Achaia, lay only half a hundred miles distant to the southward, and thither I next took my way.

In ruins a century ago, it had been rebuilt by Julius Caesar and rapidly grown to be one of the world's great commercial cities. To the colony of Roman soldiers whom Caesar settled there had been added a thriving population of Greeks and Jews. Its three harbors teemed with shipping.

Situated at the slender isthmus—only three miles wide

at its narrowest point—that separates the Aegean from a gulf of the Ionian Sea, it is a natural crossroads of world trade.

When I arrived there * I found the city buzzing with excitement and industry. The emperor Nero—he in whose clutches I now find myself—had undertaken to pierce the isthmus with a canal. Not the first to conceive of such an enterprise, he nevertheless appeared more determined than any earlier planner to carry the project to conclusion.

Swarms of slaves and laborers drudged daily on the narrow ribbon of land, digging a ditch that grew ever wider and deeper, yet never wide enough nor deep enough to serve its end. In time, like all the others who had projected it, Nero abandoned the task as impossible of achievement. Would that he had given to that work the energy he has since expended in persecuting our Christian faith!

Arriving in Corinth, I found a certain Jew named Aquila and his wife, Priscilla, with whom I made my home. Aquila was a native of far-off Pontus, near the eastern end of the Black Sea. He had gone to live at Rome, but when the emperor Claudius banished all Jews from the imperial city, Aquila and his wife had found refuge in Corinth.

They were skilled in the same craft that I had mastered, the art of tent-making, and it was convenient that I should live and work with them. As we wrought to-

* 52 A.D.

gether over the coarse haircloth, I told them of the Savior, and they believed.

Silas and Timothy came down from Macedonia to join me, and soon we had the nucleus of a Christian community in Corinth.

As was my custom, I went to the synagogue on the Sabbath to reason with the Jews, and on week-days I talked with the Greeks and other Gentiles in the marketplace, or wherever my work took me.

Here, as elsewhere, the Jews were unreceptive to my teaching. The more fervently I pleaded with them in the synagogue, the more they were inflamed against me. Their mounting anger led to bitter outbursts as they opposed my preaching of the Christ. At length, I despaired of making any progress with them.

"Your ruin be upon your own heads," I cried to them one day when they had heaped abuse upon me until I shook my robes by way of protest. "I am not responsible for your errors. Henceforth I shall go to the Gentiles!"

And I walked out of the synagogue.

A man named Justus, good and true, who lived not far from the synagogue, took me into his household. There began the meetings of the church in Corinth.

Many converts came to join us. Even Crispus, the chief ruler of the synagogue, became a member of our communion, with all the members of his household. Others came in great numbers to be baptized.

God in his mercy encouraged me and reassured me against the mounting hatred of the Jews.

"Do not be afraid," said he, appearing to me in a night vision. "Speak, and do not remain silent. For I am with you, and no man shall attack you to hurt you. For I have many people in this city."

I stayed in Corinth a year and six months, teaching the word of God among these people.

The Jews, more and more enraged by the growth of our congregation, and especially by the conversion of Crispus and other leading members of the synagogue, determined to take some action against me.

When a new proconsul, Gallio, a brother of the philosopher, Seneca, was sent out from Rome to Corinth, they thought their chance had come. They haled me into court before the new official.

"This fellow," they shouted when they appeared before the governor, "is persuading men to worship God contrary to the law."

I made ready to speak in my own defense, but it was not necessary. Gallio threw the case out of court.

"If this were a matter of a wrongful act or wicked knavery," said he to them, "reason would oblige me to listen to you Jews. But since it is only a question of words and names and your Jewish law, you will have to look after it, for I will be no judge of such matters."

He ordered them out of the court. But before they could withdraw, the Gentiles who had come to hear the case set upon Sosthenes, who had succeeded Crispus as chief ruler of the synagogue, and gave him a beating in the very presence of the governor.

Gallio took no official notice of what was going on,

and let them beat the Jewish leader. He seemed to think the beating was deserved. From that time on, our church at Corinth felt itself safer from Jewish attack.

* * *

It was during my stay at Corinth that I wrote two letters to the church at Thessalonica * which, since that time, have been followed by a stream of other epistles to Christian communities in many different cities.

The Thessalonian Christians had shown themselves worthy of praise and commendation. Their loyalty had been demonstrated when Jason and his friends, during our visit to the city, had put up bond for our security, and saved us from mistreatment at the hands of the authorities.

Some time had passed since then, and the church continued to prosper in spite of hardships. Timothy had paid a visit to the church at my direction, and he now brought to me at Corinth good reports of their conduct.

In my first letter, I told the church what good tidings of their faith and brotherly love had been brought to me by Timothy. I counseled them to maintain the utmost purity of life, and to cultivate such habits of industry as they had seen me show, when I was among them, by working at my trade in order not to be a burden to them. For there were some who seemed to think they should be supported by the church.

---

* 51-52 A.D. The Epistles to the Thessalonians appear to have been written from Corinth, rather than from Athens, as stated in the note inserted at the end of each Epistle in the Bible.

Some of them were fearful that friends who had died would not be present at the second coming of our Lord. To those I wrote such words of comfort as I could devise, assuring them that those who have fallen asleep, like those who are awake, shall all partake in the resurrection.

"Rejoice evermore. Pray without ceasing. In every thing give thanks: for this is the will of God," I wrote, and asked that this first letter be read to all the congregation.

A second letter followed shortly afterwards, quieting their fears that a terrible day of judgment would come soon upon them, and asking that they pray for us, in all our daily labors, that we might be delivered from unreasonable and wicked men. These and other matters made up the two epistles to the Thessalonians which, I am told, are still cherished in their church.

I did not realize, as I wrote these letters, that they were the first in a series of many that I should indite to different churches.

*　*　*

My long labors at Corinth having borne such satisfactory fruit, it seemed advisable for me to return to the Eastern lands.

I was eager to be at Jerusalem for the feast of Pentecost, and Priscilla and Aquila were on the point of sailing for Ephesus. We took ship together from Corinth's port of Cenchreae. For Aquila, the departure was an event of double significance. Not only did it mean, for him, the end of a long sojourn in Europe, but it also marked the termination of a vow that he had made.

In gratitude for some blessing or deliverance that had been his—I do not recall exactly what it was—he had gone unshaven for many months. His long hair and beard attracted attention wherever he went. But just before we sailed, the season of his vow expired, and he allowed his hair and beard to be trimmed. No doubt his wife, Priscilla, rejoiced that the period of his pledge had now elapsed, and her good spouse was himself again.

We were a happy trio as we sailed eastward across the Aegean, among the islands of the Greek archipelago. We gave thanks almost hourly for the generous harvest of our labors, and prayed for the prosperity and growth of our church.

When we reached Ephesus, Priscilla and Aquila remained, but I tarried there only a few days. I visited the synagogue and reasoned with the Jews. They would have had me stay longer among them, but I could not.

"I must by all means be at Jerusalem for the feast," I told them. "But I will return to you, God willing. Farewell."

I then took ship for Caesarea, and went up to Jerusalem for the feast. My visit there was brief. The solemn festival being past, and my respects having been paid to the elders and the church, I went immediately to Antioch, thus terminating the second of my major missionary journeys in the city where it had started, and which was now the chief city of our church in all the Eastern lands.

That journey had carried me through several provinces on the Asiatic mainland and across to Europe, through much of Macedonia and Greece. As companions through much of it I had had Silas, Timothy and Luke. I had been scourged and imprisoned at Philippi, hounded out of Thessalonica, scoffed at in Athens, opposed by the Jews in Corinth.

But I had felt the power and presence of God through all my travels, had been guided by visions at Troas and Corinth; had healed the fortune-telling slave, been delivered from prison and healed of my wounds at Philippi; had been shielded by friends at Thessalonica; had shaken the hold of idolatry on Athens, and had been spared from persecution, and made friends with Priscilla and Aquila, at Corinth.

Surveying the balance sheet of the journey, I felt that it had been profitable. The word of God had been preached and churches founded in places so varied as the towns of Phrygia and Galatia on the one hand, and at the seat of Greek learning and culture on the other. European cities had for the first time been evangelized. The gospel was well forward on its westward march.

Twelve

YET I could not be content to remain in Antioch. My thoughts were with the churches I had established. Reports came to me of progress here, or difficulties there, and I felt I must be off to rejoice with some, or to labor with others.

After a time in Antioch, I departed on my third missionary journey. This, in its early stages, led me along much the same route as my second. I visited and confirmed the churches in Syria, Cilicia, Lycaonia, Galatia and Phrygia, and came at last to Ephesus, the proud metropolis of the Roman province of Asia.

If the condition I had found in Athens was disturbing, that in Ephesus was equally so, but in a different fashion. Athens was given over to idolatry in the sense that the people worshiped dozens of gods, represented by a thousand different statues and temples. In Ephesus, the idolatry was equally appalling, but with this difference: the city was devoted to the worship of a single false goddess, Diana. There were shrines to her everywhere, and a magnificent temple in her honor dominated the city.

Around this building a host of legends clustered. The image of Diana which it contained was supposed to have fallen down from heaven. A tale was told even about the discovery of the marble of which it was built. The story goes that, at the time when the people were searching for suitable stone for building the temple, a shepherd named Pixodorus came running to his fellow citizens with a specimen of the whitest marble.

Upon being asked where he had found it, he gave this explanation:

"While I was feeding my flock on the slope of this very hill within the city, two of my rams fell to fighting. One of them charged the other and, missing his aim, broke with his horn this fragment from a projecting rock."

This was the desired marble. The shepherd's name was at once changed to Evangelus, meaning "Giver of Glad Tidings," and divine honors were paid to him.

I relate this as a sample of the tales that were told about every aspect of the worship of this Diana of the Ephesians.

This temple, which has few equals among the world's great structures, stood glittering at the head of the harbor, the object of the pride and superstitious devotion of the citizens. It is said that Alexander the Great offered the city all the spoils of his eastern campaign, if he might

be permitted to inscribe his name upon the temple; but
the Ephesians, in their pride, refused his offer.

Within the colonnades of this gigantic and impressive
building was carried on a strange ritual, of Greek and
Oriental elements combined, in honor of the insignifi-
cant wooden idol which it housed. There were eunuch
priests, and a swarm of virgin priestesses, and a multitude of slaves who did the menial work about the shrine.
Stored in the vaults of the temple was such a treasure
as was not to be found elsewhere in the Eastern Mediterranean lands, amassed from the gifts of superstitious
worshipers in many nations.

Combatting this lavish display of heathenism was a
little group of Christians. Aquila and Priscilla, since their
arrival here, had been active in strengthening the church
of Ephesus.

Some time before my arrival, there had come to Ephesus a Jew from Alexandria named Apollos, who had
gained some understanding of the Christ and who became a prominent member of the Ephesian church. He
was a learned man, eloquent, and capable of doing much
good, or much harm, to our cause.

Aquila and Priscilla, having heard him speaking boldly
in the synagogue, took him into their household and gave
him further instruction in the Christian way of life. He
was an earnest disciple, and grew daily in faith and understanding.

Apollos was eager to go to Greece, and in time he departed for Corinth, bearing letters from the church in

Ephesus, introducing him to the Corinthians as one who could be helpful to our cause.

Now Apollos was especially qualified to serve us in Corinth, because he had the qualities most needed to deal with the situation that prevailed there. This situation was deplorable.

The morals of that city had sunk to such a level that its very name was used to indicate depravity. The word "Corinthianize" was coined to express the last degree of wantonness. Even our own Christian community there was invaded by this moral laxity.

At the bottom of this were two factors. First, there was an active Judaizing party which sought to bind and limit our communion to the customs and practices of the Jews. And second, there was a philosophizing tendency that sapped the foundations of our faith by pretending that all laws of right and wrong were in abeyance.

With both these elements, Apollos was especially equipped to deal. First, he was a Jew who knew the ancient Scriptures and could speak boldly in the synagogue. Second, being an Alexandrian, he had been brought in contact with all the schools of philosophy and was able to deal skillfully with their sophistries.

Apollos plunged into his work at Corinth with his usual zeal, and made some progress. He found some of the Judaizers very bitter against me for various reasons, or for no reasons at all. Some claimed that I could not speak with authority, because I had not personally known Jesus. They claimed to be followers of Peter, or of James, the brother of Jesus. Others were displeased with me because I had chosen to live unmarried, and counseled others to do likewise.

Apollos reasoned skillfully with them on these points, and convinced some of the error of their ways. A number of them attached themselves personally to Apollos, describing themselves as his disciples.

This I must say of Apollos. He never took advantage of his position to serve his own interests, as opposed to those of the church. There were ample opportunities for this, but he spurned them. Moreover, he remained loyal to me through everything. We were not competitors, but fellow workers. I planted, Apollos watered, but God gave the increase.

When I arrived at Ephesus, Apollos was still at Corinth. I heard much of him from Aquila and Priscilla, and we had frequent news of him from Corinth. For there was much commerce between Ephesus and Corinth, and the two cities were linked by many bonds of common interest and trade.

During my first three months at Ephesus, I went each Sabbath to the synagogue and voiced the Truth. But at the end of that time, the opposition among the Jews had hardened. Many would not believe, and spoke evil of me wherever they went.

Thereupon, I again abandoned the Jews to their own devices, and directed my teaching to the Gentiles. A certain Tyrannus who had a following as a wise man became interested in our doctrines, and placed his lecture-hall at our disposal. There I spoke daily, our congregation met regularly, our church grew steadily in numbers, and its influence began to be felt throughout the city of Diana. This went on for two years, and both Jews and Greeks throughout the province of Asia heard the words of Jesus. Through my ministry, many were healed of sickness, and the demented were restored to reason.

So steeped in superstition were the Ephesians that many of them took my works, which seemed to them miraculous, to be mere magic, or sleight-of-hand. The city abounded in false magicians, who preyed upon the credulity of the people, and some of them tried to steal my formula for success. For it seemed to them that I must have some magic formula for healing. They went about trying to cast out evil spirits by muttering or shouting over those possessed of them such words as:

"I command you by Jesus, whom Paul preaches, to depart!"

A chief priest of the Jews, one Sceva, had seven sons who were much given to this sort of thing. They decided to make an experiment on a particularly severe case.

Going to the house of a man who was possessed of an evil spirit, they formed a ring around him and, after the usual preliminaries they had learned at their school for magicians, tried the new formula.

"We command you by Jesus, whom Paul preaches, to depart!" they chorused.

The results were disappointing.

"Jesus I know, and Paul I know," shouted the man possessed, "but who are you?"

And he leaped upon them so fiercely, and beat them

all seven so unmercifully, and tore at them so savagely, that they fled from his house half-naked and wounded.

The story of this went around Ephesus like wildfire, gathering embellishments as it traveled from mouth to mouth, with the result that magic lost much of its hold upon the people and the name of the Lord was magnified.

Many were added to our communion by this and other similar incidents; devotees of magic brought their mystical books together and made a great bonfire of them, although the value of the books burned was estimated as high as 50,000 pieces of silver. So mightily grew the word of God and prevailed!

These minor superstitions having been dealt a serious blow, those who stood to profit by the city's major superstition, the worship of Diana, became alarmed.

Chief among these were the silversmiths, who made vast quantities of little replicas of the supposedly holy image of Diana, which people carried about with them as charms or used as shrines in their homes. This practice had made the guild of silversmiths one of the most prosperous corporations in all Asia.

A man named Demetrius, one of the leaders in the guild, sensed the harm that our teaching might do to this superstitious worship of Diana, so profitable to them, and determined to do something about it. He called the members of the craft together and made them a speech on the subject.

"You men know," he said to them, "that our prosperity depends upon this traffic. You also observe that,

not only at Ephesus, but almost throughout Asia, this
fellow Paul has turned many away from this worship,
by saying that there are no gods which are made with
hands.

"As a result, not only is our trade in danger of being
seriously injured, but the temple of the great goddess
Diana may fall into disrepute, and the magnificence of
her whom all Asia and the world now worship, may be
destroyed."

When the silverworkers heard his words, they were
very angry.

"Great is Diana of the Ephesians," they cried, and
ran about the city raising a tumult.

They laid hold on Gaius and Aristarchus, two of my
traveling companions from Macedonia, and rushed them
off to the amphitheater.

When I heard what was happening, I wanted to
hurry to their aid, but the disciples restrained me, and
some of the leading men of the province, who were
friendly toward me, urged me not to go into the amphitheater. They seemed certain that the excitement would
die down quickly if I myself did not appear on the scene.

Meanwhile, a vast concourse of people rushed to the
meeting-place, most of them in ignorance of what was
happening, but curious to learn the reason for the tumult. They found a scene of complete confusion, some
people shouting one thing and some another.

A Jew named Alexander tried to make a speech to the
multitude, but as soon as they knew that he was a Jew,
they shouted him down.

"Great is Diana of the Ephesians," they screamed, and kept it up for about two hours.

Finally the town clerk appeared, and quieted the crowd so that he could make himself heard.

"Fellow Ephesians," he said, "what man is there that does not know that the city of the Ephesians worships the great goddess Diana, and her image which fell down from Jupiter?"

This brought a great outburst of applause, and the speaker was allowed to continue.

"Since this cannot be disputed," continued the official, "you ought to be quiet, and do nothing rashly. But you have brought here these men, who are neither robbers of churches, nor blasphemers of your goddess.

"If Demetrius and his fellow craftsmen have a case against any man, the law is open to them, and there are magistrates. Let them bring their case to court. If you desire anything else, it will have to be settled in a lawful assembly.

"We are liable to be called to account for this day's uproar, since there is no reason that we can give to justify it.

"Go to your homes, and abide by the orderly processes of law."

The vast assemblage, quieted and reassured by his words, dispersed at once.

The church at Ephesus had thus been guided and protected through a difficult crisis. The danger was not yet past, but we had at least been shielded against an outbreak of violent persecution.

Lest I should embarrass the church by my continued presence—since the hatred of the Ephesians seemed to be focused upon my person—I determined again to take to the road, or rather, to sea.

This time, my path lay directly to the west: to Macedonia and Greece.

Thirteen

—

THE STATE of affairs in Corinth continued to be of great concern to me. I paid a brief visit to the city and found the condition of the public morals, and even of the Christian community there, to be lamentably low. Apollos sent me distressing reports, and the frequent visitors from Corinth to Ephesus had little that was encouraging to say of what went on there.

I had written a severe letter to members of the church in Corinth * and in reply received from the loyal ones a plea for advice * on how to deal with the serious problems confronting them.

It was in reply to this request that I wrote a rather long epistle designed to answer their doubts and calm their fears.† I tried to heal the divisions among them, for there were some who said that they followed me, and others

* These epistles have not been preserved.
† The First Epistle to the Corinthians.

Apollos, and others Peter, and still others the Christ; not knowing that we are all one in Christ.

I sought to win them away from intellectual sophistries, and to turn them to the simple faith that men feel in their hearts, the wisdom of God. I warned them against immorality, and counseled discipline against those who broke the moral law. I urged them not to sue each other in the courts, as some were doing, but to submit their cases to arbitration among themselves.

A host of questions about marriage I tried to answer well and wisely. Temperance in all things I urged upon them, and abhorrence of idols, and brotherly love. I refuted with all my power the claim of some that there is no resurrection from the dead.

And having dispatched this letter to Corinth, I myself took leave of Ephesus and traveled into Macedonia, to Philippi.

Here, where Silas and I had been so miraculously freed from prison, the church had grown strong and free from serious fault, and loyal always to me its founder. Here was my beloved Timothy. And soon arrived Titus from Corinth, with better tidings: how the church there had purged itself of evildoers and impostors.

Pleased with this news, I immediately sent Titus back to Corinth, bearing another letter.* I rejoiced with the Corinthians in their faithfulness, and commended their good deeds.

Exhorting them to further holiness, even in the face

* The Second Epistle to the Corinthians.

of persecution, I narrated to them the tortures to which
I myself had been subjected; tortures which I have not
wished to number elsewhere, nor to emphasize unduly.
Yet if I had endured such things, they might indeed
endure the lighter hardships that would be their lot.

At that time, I had on five different occasions been
flogged by the Jews, receiving thirty-nine stripes each
time. Thrice had I been beaten with rods, once stoned.
Three times had I been shipwrecked, and spent a night
and a day in the deep.

I had suffered in journeyings often, in peril of floods
and of robbers; in danger from my own countrymen, and
from the heathen; in peril in cities, in the wilderness, at
sea, and among false and treacherous companions.
Weariness and pain I had known, and long, weary
watches, hunger and thirst, fasting, cold and nakedness.
Frequently I had been in prison, and often near death.

If I, who was physically weak, could endure these
things, might not they also bear such light burdens as
would be laid upon them? I adjured them to hold themselves strong in the faith until I should come soon to
visit them.

And having dispatched this letter by Titus to the
Corinthians, I traveled on westward to Illyricum and the
Adriatic and, after some time, myself went on to
Corinth.

Here I found that my letters had done much good.
In spite of lingering hatred in some quarters, I found
that most of the congregation were loyal and friendly to

me. The foundations of the Corinthian church had been greatly strengthened, and corruption driven out.

But although Truth had won a victory at Corinth, there were disturbing reports from the churches in Galatia. It seemed that I had no sooner cast down evils in one place than they arose to mock me in another.

I therefore wrote from Corinth to these congregations,* recalling how deep was my affection for them, remembering as I did their great kindness to me when I was ill.

The difficulty in Galatia was that the Judaizers were at work, trying to make Jews of Christians, and persuading them that, even in order to be Christians, they must be circumcised, and submit to the customs and practices of the Jews.

In refuting their contentions, I recalled the decisions of the council at Jerusalem, many years before, where it had been decided that converts to Christianity need not be circumcised, and I again related how I had withstood Peter to the face when, at Antioch, he had seemed to falter in his adherence to that decree.

"O foolish Galatians," I wrote to them, "who has bewitched you, that you should not obey Truth? Now, after you have known God, or rather are known to God, how is it that you turn again to these weak and worthless notions, to which you are again willing to be held in bondage? I am alarmed about you, lest I have bestowed my labor upon you in vain."

No sooner was this letter dispatched to Galatia than

* The Epistle to the Galatians.

news of other troubles arrived from an entirely different quarter, and I was obliged to indite a letter to the church at Rome.*

This church I had had no share in founding, having never been at Rome up to that time. But word of the faithfulness of its members, in the midst of a sinful and idolatrous city, had often reached me, and I longed to visit the brave disciples there. Little did I think that, when I did visit Rome, it would be in chains!

It happened that Phoebe, a deaconess of the church at Cenchreae, near Corinth, was going to Rome on a matter of business—being a woman of property—and I sent my letter to the Roman church by her hand, commending her to the congregation there, which included many of my dearest friends. Aquila and Priscilla were now again in Rome, and the church was meeting in their house; they had been pillars of the church both at Corinth and at Ephesus, and had risked their lives in my behalf. Also at Rome were my distant kinsmen Andronicus, Junias and Herodion. To all these and to many others, I sent greetings by the worthy Phoebe.

Lest, in the midst of temptations and persecutions, their faith should waver, I sent them words of cheer and comfort.

"I am persuaded," I bore witness to them, "that neither death, nor life, nor angels, nor principalities, nor powers, nor things present, nor things to come, nor height, nor depth, nor any other created thing, shall be

* The Epistle to the Romans.

able to separate us from the love of God, which is in Christ Jesus our Lord."

The reason why I could not come to them at Rome at that time was that I had been engaged for many months, along with Titus and others of the disciples, in raising a collection for the needy and distressed brothers at Jerusalem.

We had raised some funds in Macedonia, and for more than a year the Christians of Achaia had been laying aside something on the first day of every week for this purpose. This money was now collected and entrusted to treasurers elected by the churches. It was necessary for me to go with the treasurers to Jerusalem and deliver this offering of love, from the Gentile Christians of Greece to the Jewish Christians of Palestine.

Just as we were on the point of sailing from the port of Cenchreae, we learned that some of the Jews of Corinth were plotting to seize and murder me as I went aboard the ship. I therefore abruptly changed my plans, and departed secretly by way of Macedonia. Again, through divine providence, my enemies were thwarted in their efforts to destroy me.

Having briefly visited the churches of Macedonia, we sailed for the Troad, on the Asiatic coast. I had twice before paid brief visits to this historic region. This time, I tarried there a week.

On the evening before we were to take our leave, the members of the church were all gathered together in an upper room to partake of the communion, and I preached to them until midnight.

The hour growing late, a young man named Eutychus went to sleep as he sat in the opening of a window, and fell to the ground below. The disciples were much dismayed, but I went down to him, and embraced him, and found that he was still alive.

"Do not be alarmed," I said to those who had gathered around. "His life is still in him."

We carried him into the upper room again, and there we partook of the communion, and I continued my discourse until the break of day, and then departed.

The disciples were greatly comforted, for we had restored the young man to life and strength, and all was well.

Thus was the power of God revealed in the ancient land of Troas.

In order that I might have a little more time with the disciples there, I did not go aboard the ship with my companions when it was ready to sail, but arranged to join them at Assos, about twenty miles down the coast. The distance to Assos by sea around the cape was nearly twice as far, so that I was enabled to prolong my time with our friends at Troas, and then walk to Assos along the road through the oak woods, enjoying the quiet countryside and the pleasure of walking after much travel at sea.

At Assos, magnificent with its walls, gates and terraces, its theater and citadel, I went aboard our ship when it arrived, and we sailed on southward.

Passing along the eastern shore of Lesbos, we glimpsed

the city of Mytelene, the beautiful capital of the poetess
Sappho's domain, and lay overnight in the shelter of
the island. Next day, we sailed on past the island of
Chios, or Scio, of whose lighthearted people it is said
that "It is easier to find a green horse than a sober-
minded Sciot."

Another day brought us to the island of Samos, and
we anchored for the night at Trogyllium. Then on to
Miletus, on the mainland.

Miletus was only thirty miles from Ephesus. Being
eager to continue to Jerusalem, and arrive there for the
feast of Pentecost, I could not take the time to go to
Ephesus, where I had lived and worked. But I sent word
to the disciples that I was near at hand, at Miletus,
and the elders of the church came down to meet me
there.

Here we assembled at a place on the shore, and I
addressed them. For several days, I had had a keen intu-
ition that I should meet with imprisonment and suffering if I went to Jerusalem, yet I could not but continue
on my way. It seemed imperative that I should deliver
into the hands of the apostles there the collection that
had been raised for them in Macedonia and Greece.
Not to go on to the Holy City would have been a
breach of duty. This feeling I shared with the elders from
Ephesus who met with me on the beach at Miletus.

"I am now on my way to Jerusalem," I told them,
"impelled by a sense of duty. I do not know what shall
befall me there, but the Holy Spirit, in town after town

that I have visited, has warned me that imprisonment and afflictions await me.

"Yet none of these things move me, nor do I count my life dear to myself, so long as I may be permitted to finish my course with joy, and complete the ministry entrusted to me by Jesus, of bearing witness to the glad tidings of the grace of God.

"I know that, after my departing, grievous wolves will enter in among you, not sparing the flock. Also among yourselves men will arise who speak perverse things, to draw away disciples after them. Therefore watch, and remember that for three years—while I lived at Ephesus —I did not cease to warn every one of you night and day.

"And now, brothers, I commend you to God, and to the word of his grace, which is able to build you up, and to give you an inheritance among all those who are sanctified.

"You shall see my face no more," I told them, convinced that I was saying farewell forever. Yet God in His good grace has brought me back to Ephesus since then, to see the growth and prosperity of His church.

When I had spoken, I kneeled down and prayed with them all. They wept, and threw their arms about my neck, and kissed me, grieving because I had said that they would see my face no more. With loving gestures, they accompanied me to the ship. It was with difficulty that I tore myself from their caresses, so that we could sail away on our mission.

From Miletus, we sped southward past the isle of

Patmos to Cos, an island with a city of the same name
which was a seat of medical lore, the birthplace of
Hippocrates. Thence, on the day following, our course
took us to Rhodes, famous for its roses, its climate, and
as a center of shipbuilding. The great Colossus that had
once stood at an entrance to its harbor was in ruins,
having been overthrown by an earthquake.

From Rhodes our ship carried us to Patara where,
finding another vessel ready to sail in the direction we
were taking, we went aboard and set forth. The isle of
Cyprus, its highest mountains capped with snow, lay
on our left as we sailed across the open sea to Tyre, for
which port the ship had a cargo.

In this busy commercial city of Phoenicia, widely
known for its dyestuffs and its glassware, we remained
for seven days, with disciples whom we found there.
These good friends tried to dissuade me from going to
Jerusalem, having been warned by the Holy Spirit that
I should meet with danger in that city.

Yet I determined to press on, and when the time came
for our ship to sail, these good Christians, with their
wives and children, came with us to the very water's
edge, and kneeled down and prayed with us on the
shore, and took fond leave of us as we entered the ship
to continue on our way.

Our next port was Ptolemais,* where we spent but a
single day with the church in that city, and then went
on to Caesarea.

* The modern Acre.

Here Philip, who had earlier been appointed one of the seven deacons to look after the affairs of the church in Jerusalem, was now residing. He took us into his house. He and his four daughters, who were young women of great virtue, offered us every hospitality.

While we tarried at Caesarea, there came down from Judea the man named Agabus, renowned for his skill in prophecy, the same who, some years before, had brought to Barnabas and me at Antioch the warning that a famine was at hand in Judca.

Agabus seemed destined to be a bearer of bad tidings. He came to see me at Philip's house and, in the presence of the brothers there assembled, gave me a dramatic warning of the dangers that might confront me in Jerusalem. Taking my girdle from about me, he bound his own hands and feet with it.

"The Holy Spirit," he declared, "has said to me, 'So shall the Jews at Jerusalem bind the man who owns this girdle, and shall deliver him into the hands of the Gentiles.'"

Thereupon Luke and my other companions, and the Christians of Caesarea, tearfully urged me not to go to Jerusalem. But I would not forsake my purpose.

"What do you mean by this weeping?" I asked them. "Your grief is breaking my heart. Yet I am ready not only to be bound, but even to die at Jerusalem for the name of the Lord Jesus."

When they saw that they could not dissuade me, they ceased their entreaties, saying, "God's will be done."

So my companions and I went up to Jerusalem, along with some of the disciples from Caesarea, and lodged in the house of Mnason, a native of Cyprus, who was one of the first to join our congregation.

Fourteen

———

W HEN we arrived in Jerusalem, the disciples received us warmly, and the next day we appeared before James the brother of Jesus and all the other elders of the church.

We presented the collection that had been made in the churches of the Gentile lands, and I gave a report of the achievements of my mission during the four years since I was last in Jerusalem.

They gave thanks to God for our successes.

But after this was done, they had a request to make of me. They led up to it cautiously, and with lengthy explanations.

"You can see, brother," they said to me, "how many thousands of Jews there are who believe, and they are all zealous upholders of the Jewish law. They have been told that you are teaching all the Jews who live among the Gentiles to forsake the Mosaic law, by saying that they ought neither to circumcise their children, nor to observe the ancient Jewish customs. They will hear that you are here, and an angry throng is sure to gather. Therefore, do this thing that we tell you.

"We have four men here—four Jewish Christians—who have taken upon themselves a Nazaritic vow, such as is taken to express gratitude for deliverance from danger, or in some such case. They have let their hair grow, have abstained from wine for the necessary period, and have otherwise fulfilled the requirements of their vow. Now is the time for them to go to the temple to be liberated from their vow with the proper ceremonies.

"Take these men, go through the rites of purification with them, and assist them in defraying the expenses of the ceremonies. Then they will publicly shave their heads. As a result of your sharing in the ritual, everyone will know that the things which have been said about you are not true, and that you live an orderly life and fulfill the requirements of the law."

In compliance with these directions, and desiring to maintain peace within the church at Jerusalem, I took the four men in charge, went through the ceremonies with them next day, and then went with them to the temple, to give notice that the days of their purification were concluded. I remained in attendance until the required sacrifices had been offered for each of them.

This was a long and tedious process. Each of them brought the following offerings to the temple: one he lamb, less than a year old, without blemish, for a sin offering; one ewe lamb, less than a year old, without blemish, for a sin offering; one ram without blemish for peace offerings; a basket of unleavened bread; cakes of fine flour mixed with oil; wafers of unleavened bread anointed with oil; a meat offering; and drink offerings.

All these things were handed over to a priest, who proceeded in turn to sacrifice on the altar the ewe lamb and the he lamb, and then the ram with the basket of unleavened bread, then the meat offering and the drink offering.

On entering the inner court of the temple, each of the four men had caused his head to be shaved, and now took the hair which had been shorn off and put it in the fire under the ram that was being sacrificed as a peace offering. The priest then took the shoulder of the ram, and one unleavened cake out of the basket, and one unleavened wafer, and placed them on the hands of the person offering the vow, and waved them before the altar.

It took some time, and required several visits to the temple, before all this elaborate formula could be gone through for all four of the men, but, in obedience to my instructions, I remained within the temple enclosure throughout the ceremonies.

Just as they were drawing to a close, I was set upon by a band of ruffianly fellows. They were led by some Jews from Ephesus who, having come to Jerusalem, saw me in the temple and were determined, having failed to bring about my undoing in their own city, to accomplish it here.

They had seen me in the city with a Gentile Christian from Ephesus, and pretended to believe that I had taken this man into the temple enclosure with me. This would have been a serious offense, as no Gentile was permitted to proceed to the inner courts. It was the one offense for which the Jews, under Roman law, could put a man to death without appeal to the Roman authorities.

"Men of Israel, help!" they cried, and gathered a crowd of temple worshipers around them to do me harm.

"This is the man that teaches all men everywhere against the Jewish people, and the Jewish law, and this temple. Moreover, he has brought Greeks into the temple, and polluted this holy place!"

Whereupon they seized me, and dragged me out of the temple. The temple police, fearing further disturbances, closed the gates behind us.

The mob beat me unmercifully, but suddenly desisted when a body of Roman soldiers appeared on the scene. Word of the disturbance had been carried to Claudius Lysias, commander of the garrison in the fortress of Antonia, adjoining the temple enclosure; he had summoned some of his officers and a body of men and rushed to the place where my assailants had dragged me.

As soon as I had been separated from the mob, the commander ordered me to be chained by each hand to a soldier.

"Who is this man?" he demanded. "And what has he done?"

Some of the crowd cried one thing, and others another. Claudius Lysias saw that it was not possible to learn the facts from these people, and ordered me to be taken to the fortress.

As we marched across the outer court of the temple and up some stairs, the press of the throng was so great that the soldiers closed in around me and almost carried me, to protect me from them.

"Away with him!" the mob kept crying. "Away with him!"

Just as I was being led into the fortress, where the garrison was quartered, I made a request of Claudius Lysias.

"May I speak with you, sir?" I asked him in Greek.

"What!" cried he in amazement, "can you speak Greek? Are you not that Egyptian who some years ago raised an insurrection of four thousand ruffians, and led them out into the wilderness?"

"No," said I. "I am a Jew, a citizen of Tarsus in Cilicia, which is a city of no slight importance. I pray you, allow me to speak to the people."

He granted my request. As we mounted the stairs leading to the fortress, I turned and, motioning as best I could with my chained hands to the crowd for silence, addressed them in the Hebrew tongue.

"Brothers," I said, "hear my defense."

When they heard that I spoke Hebrew, they were silent.

"I am a Jew," I told them, "born in Tarsus in Cilicia, but brought up in this city at the feet of the great teacher

Gamaliel, and taught according to the perfect manner of our forefathers. I was zealous in God's work, as you are now. I persecuted this new faith to the death, binding and delivering into prisons both men and women."

I told them how I had gone to Damascus to persecute the Nazarenes, and how I had seen a vision and been converted; how I had been struck blind, and had my sight restored to me.

"Then when I came again to Jerusalem," I continued, "while I was praying in the temple, I fell as it were into a trance. I saw the Lord Jesus, and he said to me, 'Hurry, and depart quickly from Jerusalem, for they will not believe what you tell them concerning me.'

" 'Lord,' said I, 'they know that I imprisoned and beat those in every synagogue who believed in you; and when Stephen was stoned, I stood by, and consented to his death, and held the garments of those who killed him.'

"Then said Jesus to me, 'Depart, for I will send you far away, to the Gentiles.' "

The moment I had said this, the mob went wild with anger, casting off their garments, and gathering up handfuls of dust to fling into the air as a sign of their anger.

"Away with such a fellow from the earth," they cried, "for it is not fitting that he should live."

So enraged were they because I had said that I had been divinely appointed to preach Truth not to them, but to Gentiles, and in distant lands.

Claudius Lysias, much perplexed by all this turmoil,

ordered the soldiers to take me into the fortress and flog me until I confessed what wrong I had done.

I was taken in and bound, but before the lash was laid upon me I spoke to the officer in charge.

"Is it lawful for you to flog a Roman citizen, even one who has been convicted of no wrong?" I asked him.

This surprised him greatly. He told the soldiers to wait, and went off to consult his commander.

"What are you intending to do to this man?" he asked Claudius Lysias. "He claims to be a Roman citizen."

The commander, surprised in his turn, came down from his quarters to see me.

"Tell me, are you a Roman citizen?" he asked.

"Yes," said I.

"I paid a large sum for my citizenship," he mused.

"But I was born a Roman citizen," I told him.

He at once dismissed the soldiers who were to have beaten me. I could see that he was much disturbed because he had bound me, now that he knew I was entitled to the privileges of Roman citizenship. From then on, I was well treated.

Next morning, in the hope of learning just what I was accused of, he ordered the Sanhedrin to meet and brought me, unfettered, before this highest court of the Jews.

I could feel their intense hatred for me. There was not the slightest chance of a fair trial before this tribunal. I had hardly opened my mouth when I found how bitter they were against me.

"Brothers," said I, beginning my defense, "My oon

science is clear that I have lived rightly before God up to this day."

This they took to be blasphemy. One of them, who I learned later was Ananias, the chief priest, ordered those who stood beside me to strike me on the mouth for having so spoken. My anger flared high.

"God will smite you, you whitewashed wall," I shouted at him. "Dare you sit there to judge me according to the law, and at the same time order me to be struck contrary to the law?"

"Dare you rail at God's high priest?" screamed those who stood beside me.

I saw that I had done wrong.

"I did not know, brothers, that he was the high priest," I said. "It is written in the law, 'You shall not speak evil of the ruler of your people,' and I have no desire to disobey the law."

Yet I did not intend to yield myself to injustice at the hands of these cruel and unfair judges. Some of them, I knew, were Pharisees and others Sadducees; there were many points of disagreement between the two factions.

I determined to make use of their antipathies in my own defense. The great point of division between them was the question of the resurrection of the dead. The Pharisees accepted it as sound doctrine, but the Sadducees maintained that there was no such thing possible.

"Brothers," I said, "I am a Pharisee, the son of a Pharisee. And here I am on trial before you because of my hope of a resurrection of the dead."

By these words, I accused the Sadducees in the Sanhedrin of having haled me before them because I
preached the doctrine of the resurrection, which was
acceptable to the Pharisees, but not to them.

Immediately there was dissension between the Pharisees and the Sadducees on the court, and the assembly
was divided. There was a great uproar. The scribes that
belonged to the Pharisees' party stood up and contended
fiercely.

"We find no evil in this man," they shouted. "If a
spirit or an angel has spoken to him, let us not fight
against God!"

By this time, the two factions in the council were
fighting each other so bitterly that Claudius Lysias, fearing they would tear me to pieces in their quarreling,
ordered the soldiers to take me away from among them,
and lead me back to the fortress.

*　　*　　*

Next night, the Lord appeared again to me in a vision
and said,

"Be of good cheer, Paul, for even as you have testified
faithfully concerning me in Jerusalem, so must you do
also at Rome."

Although I had longed to visit Rome, this was the
first divine intimation that I should surely visit the city
on the Tiber. The prospect of the voyage made me
happy. But the manner of my coming here has been
different from that I had imagined

Meanwhile, the Jews who were most bitter against me, having been thwarted in their schemes to kill me, decided to do in secret what they had not been able to do openly. They organized themselves into a gang—more than forty of them—and took an oath that they would neither eat nor drink till they had killed me. Then they admitted the high priests and the elders into their conspiracy.

"We have bound ourselves under a great oath," they told leading members of the Sanhedrin in secret, "that we will eat nothing until we have slain this Paul. Now do you and the others of the Sanhedrin therefore request Claudius Lysias to bring Paul before you again tomorrow, as if you wished to ask further questions of him. And we shall stand ready to murder him even before he comes near the place."

But my little nephew, my sister's son, a very alert lad, heard that they were lying in wait for me, and came to the fortress and told me of the plot. I immediately called for the captain of the guard.

"Take this young man to the commander," I asked of him, "for he has something important to tell him."

The captain took the lad to Claudius Lysias and said,

"Paul the prisoner called me to him, and asked me to bring to you this young man, who has something to say to you."

Claudius Lysias, who was still worried about the mistake he had made concerning me, took my nephew by the hand and led him aside privately.

"What is it you have to tell me?" he asked.

"The Jews," said the lad, "have agreed to ask you to bring Paul down before the Sanhedrin tomorrow, pretending that they wish to question him more thoroughly. But do not consent, for more than forty of them are lying in wait for him, having bound themselves by an oath, that they will neither eat nor drink till they have killed him. They are ready now, awaiting your consent."

Claudius Lysias lost no time in acting.

First, he sent the young man away, warning him to tell no one that he had reported these things.

Then he called in two of the captains.

"Have two hundred soldiers of the legion, seventy horsemen, and two hundred spearmen ready to march at nine o'clock this evening," he commanded them. "And have mounts ready for the prisoner Paul, and deliver him safely to Felix, the governor, at Caesarea."

He then dictated the following letter:

"Claudius Lysias sends greetings to His Excellency the Governor, Felix.

"This man Paul was seized by the Jews, and would have been killed by them, but I came with troops and rescued him, having heard that he was a Roman citizen. Trying to learn what they accused him of, I brought him before their council. It then appeared that he was accused of misdemeanors under their law, but was not charged with anything deserving the death penalty or imprisonment.

"Then I was told that the Jews were lying in ambush for the man, whereupon I have sent him immediately to you, and have ordered his accusers to lay their charges against him before you.

"Farewell."

That same evening, when it was dark, I was brought out of the fortress, mounted upon a horse, and set off, in the midst of this formidable bodyguard, for Caesarea. It was evident from the size of the guard that Claudius Lysias wished to run no risk of having his prisoner seized or ambushed by the Jews.

All through the night we marched, first northward, then veering toward the west. Overhead the stars shone brightly, shedding a soft light on the mountains and valleys we traversed. The tramp of the foot-soldiers and the rattle of their armor mingled with the hoof-beats of the cavalry and the jingle of harness. Clouds of dust rose from the road and settled on us. We made a short halt at midnight, and again just before dawn.

Daybreak found us crossing the great plain of Sharon, between fields of wheat and barley. Shortly afterwards, we arrived at the town of Antipatris, where our two detachments of foot-soldiers faced about and returned to Jerusalem, leaving the troop of cavalry to continue as my escort. That afternoon, we arrived at Caesarea.

The captain of cavalry delivered Claudius Lysias' letter to the governor, Felix, and brought me before him. After having read the letter, Felix asked,

"What province are you from?"

"From Cilicia," said I.

"I will take up your case," he said, "when your accusers arrive from Jerusalem."

Then, turning to an officer of his court, he commanded:

"Keep this man in custody in Herod's judgment hall."

Thus was I saved from the anger of the Jews in Jerusalem, and brought to trial in Caesar's court, at Caesarea.

Fifteen

CAESAREA is a little piece of Rome, set down upon a distant shore. Seat of the administration of the Roman procurator, or governor, of Judea, it is a replica in miniature of this city on the Tiber.

It is a new and shining city of white stone, built only a few decades ago by Herod the Great in honor of Augustus Caesar. Where before stood only a fortress called Strato's Tower, and a meager landing-place for small ships, there is now a prosperous and impressive city, with sumptuous palaces, an amphitheater of stone and a commodious harbor.

This port was created by sinking into the sea vast stones, some 50 feet long, 18 feet wide and 9 feet high, to form a curving breakwater which shelters the harbor from the prevailing southwesterly winds.

Built by a King of Judea as a tribute to an Emperor of the Romans, the city is peopled chiefly by Greeks and

Jews, and by a polyglot throng from all the trading nations of the East. There are frequent riots and disturbances, even though it is the seat of a Roman governor.

The place is impressed upon my memory because I visited it several times, and on this occasion spent two whole years in custody there, in partial confinement, but not entirely cut off from the teeming life of the city.

Only five days after my arrival, my accusers came down from Jerusalem to lodge formal complaint against me with the governor, Felix. The delegation consisted of several members of the Sanhedrin, led by Ananias, the high priest, who had clearly not forgotten my outburst against him in the trial at Jerusalem. They brought with them as prosecutor an attorney named Tertullus, widely known for his successes in the courts.

As soon as they arrived, I was summoned to appear with them before the governor, and Tertullus began his speech of accusation. He opened with a little flattery for Felix.

"Thanks to you," he said, addressing the governor, "we enjoy great tranquillity, and great favors are shown to our people, for which, most noble Felix, we are grateful."

The governor, whom he addressed as "most noble Felix," was anything but noble; he was of servile origin, owing his position to intrigue alone, and I shall indicate how little of true nobility was to be found in his character.

"Not to detain you longer," continued Tertullus, "I

beg you, out of your clemency, to hear us for the space
of a few brief words.

"We have found this man Paul a pestilent fellow, an
inciter of sedition among the Jews throughout the
world, and a ringleader of the sect of the Nazarenes.
He even tried to profane our temple.

"We arrested him, and would have judged him according to our law, but the commander of the garrison,
Lysias, came upon us and with great violence took him
out of our hands, and commanded us, his accusers, to
lay our case before you here at Caesarea.

"By examining him yourself, you can confirm the
things that we accuse him of."

The Jews who stood about gave testimony that what
Tertullus had said was so.

The governor then made a sign to me that I might
speak in my own defense.

"Knowing that you have for many years been a judge
in this country," said I, addressing Felix, "I gladly
answer for myself.

"It was only twelve days ago that I went up to Jerusalem to worship. These people never found me in the
temple disputing with any man, nor inciting the people,
either in the synagogues or elsewhere in the city. Nor
can they prove the things they now accuse me of.

"This I confess to you: that in the way which they
describe as heresy, I worship the God of my forefathers,
believing all things that are written in the books of the
law and of the prophets. And I have hope from God,
which they themselves also profess, that there shall be

a resurrection of the dead, both of the just and of the unjust. My constant effort is to keep my conscience free of offense toward God and toward men.

"After an absence of several years, I came to Jerusalem to bring alms and goodwill offerings to my people. Certain Jews from the province of Asia found me in the temple, having performed the rites of purification, but with no throng about me, nor having caused any tumult. Those persons should be here to lay their complaint before you, if they have anything against me.

"Let these accusers who are here say whether they found me guilty of any offense when I stood before their council, except for this one thing: that as I stood before them I declared, 'The thing that you are trying me for today is my faith in the resurrection of the dead.' "

At this point Felix adjourned the hearing.

"When Claudius Lysias, the commander of the garrison, has come down from Jerusalem," he told the Jews, "I shall go fully into this matter."

And he ordered a captain to keep me in custody, but to treat me with indulgence, and not to prevent my friends from seeing me or ministering to my needs.

A few days later, Felix and his wife Drusilla, who was a Jewess, sent for me, and had me speak to them about the Christian faith.

This I did gladly, hoping that the seed of Truth might find some root even in such poor soil. For the record of Felix, and of his wife, was such that great changes were evidently needed in their way of life before they could be Christians.

Felix was the brother of a clever man named Pallas, who had become a favorite of the emperor Claudius. He (Felix) had somehow gained the friendship of one of the high priests of the Jews, named Jonathan, who helped to get him appointed procurator of Judea. But the measure of Felix's gratitude is evident from the fact that he later had his benefactor, Jonathan, murdered in the very sanctuary of the temple at Jerusalem.

It was generally agreed that Felix, although he had done the country some good, and cleared it of highway robbers, was adept in all the arts of lust and cruelty. He had got his wife, Drusilla, away from her former husband by employing the aid of a magician-soothsayer.

Marrying Drusilla was one of Felix's most ambitious achievements, for she was of the family of the Herods, a sister of King Herod Agrippa II and of Bernice, who was the daughter of one Herod and the wife of another. By linking his fortunes with those of this powerful family, Felix felt that he had assured fame and fortune for himself. But even now, his ambition was not satisfied, and he was always seeking new paths to wealth and power.

When I was brought before this regal couple, who sat arrayed in great magnificence, surrounded by every luxury, I spoke to them simply of the way of Christ, of righteousness and temperance, and of the judgment to come. Drusilla heard me with some slight show of feeling; it was at her urging, I think, that I had been called before them. She, poor woman, has since died, with her little son, in the great eruption of Vesuvius, at Pompeii.

Felix, as I talked, was ill at ease. When I spoke of righteousness and judgment, and of the fate of evil-doers, he actually trembled.

"Go now," he said when he could stand no more. "When I have a convenient opportunity, I will send for you."

Time passed, and nothing happened. I remained in custody, but with many privileges. Later on, Felix sent for me occasionally, on the pretext that he was interested in what I had to say. But it gradually appeared that what he wanted was a bribe to let me go. For this I had no money, nor would I have given it him if I had.

Thus two whole years slipped by, until Felix was relieved of his post at Caesarea and went away. He left me behind, and my case was taken up where Felix had dropped it by his successor.

The new procurator was Porcius Festus. After only three days in Caesarea upon his arrival, he went up to Jerusalem to survey the situation there.

No sooner had he reached the city, than the high priest and the leaders of the Jews approached him concerning me.

"Send him up to Jerusalem to be tried," they implored Festus. For they had again prepared an ambush, and plotted to kill me at the first opportunity.

But Festus refused. He was returning shortly to Caesarea, he told them, and I would be kept there.

"Let those among you who can do so return to Caesarea with me," he told them, "and there lodge accusations against this man, if there is any wickedness in him."

About ten days later he came down again to Caesarea,
accompanied by my accusers. And the very next day he
took his place on the official seat of judgment and caused
me to be brought before him.

The Jews who had come to Caesarea for the purpose
repeated the charges they had made against me before
Felix two years earlier, but with no more proof than they
had been able to present at that time.

I defended myself as before, denying any guilt.

"Neither against the law of the Jews, nor against their
temple, nor against Caesar, have I committed any wrong
whatever," I declared when Festus permitted me to
speak.

But the governor was anxious to be through with this
tiresome case which his predecessor had left on his
hands, and he was willing to do the Jews a favor if possible, at the beginning of his administration.

"Are you willing to go up to Jerusalem?" he asked me,
"and there stand trial before me on these charges?"

But I refused, knowing that the Jews would lead me
into an ambush.

"Here," said I, "I stand at Caesar's judgment seat,
which is the right place for me to be tried. I have done
the Jews no wrong, as you must very well know. If I
have done wrong, and committed any crime deserving
the penalty of death, I do not refuse to die. But if there
is no truth in the charges brought against me, no one
has the right to deliver me to these men. *I appeal to
Caesar!*"

By these words, I committed my cause to the highest

earthly court. It was my right as a Roman citizen to appeal my case to the emperor himself, and in this extremity I availed myself of it.

Festus consulted with his legal advisers, or assessors, as to whether my appeal was valid. They evidently answered him in the affirmative, for he turned to me and said,

"Do you indeed appeal to Caesar? Then to Caesar you shall go!"

He dismissed the Jews and gave formal notice that my case was appealed to Rome.

Festus' conduct of the hearing had been correct in every particular. He apparently found my case an interesting one, as involving certain legal points concerning the relation of the Jewish and Roman administrations. Therefore, when Herod Agrippa II, King of Trachonitis, arrived at Caesarea, with his sister Bernice, on a visit shortly afterward, Festus told Agrippa all about it. He probably thought that Herod, who was familiar with the law and the religion of the Jews, could throw some light on the matter.

"There is a certain man left in bonds by Felix," said Festus to Agrippa, "about whom the chief priests and elders of the Jews informed me, when I was at Jerusalem, and desired to have judgment pronounced against him.

"I told them, 'It is not the practice of the Romans to deliver any man to die before he has been given an opportunity to meet his accusers face to face, and speak for himself concerning the charges brought against him.'

"Therefore, when they came down here to Caesarea, without any delay on the very next day I took my place on the judgment seat and commanded the man to be brought forth.

"When his accusers spoke against him before me, they brought no such accusations as I had expected, but only raised against him certain points concerning their own religion, and about one named Jesus, who was dead, but whom this man Paul affirmed to be alive.

"Because I was at a loss how to deal with these questions, I asked Paul whether he would be willing to go to Jerusalem, and be judged there concerning these matters. But he appealed to have his case heard by the emperor, and I have therefore commanded him to be kept in custody until I can send him to Caesar."

"I should like to hear the man myself," said King Agrippa to Festus.

"Tomorrow," said Festus, "you shall hear him."

Next day, I was brought into the audience chamber of the palace, to a scene of great pomp and ceremony. To honor the royal visitor and his sister, Festus had arrayed the palace in all its finest trappings, and summoned the chief dignitaries of his province to attend in full regalia. Present were not only Festus, Agrippa and Bernice, but all the chief military men and civil personages of Caesarea.

When all had taken their appointed places, I was brought in by my guards, in chains, and stood before the royal pair. Festus opened the hearing with a speech.

"King Agrippa," said he, "and all men here present

with us, here you see the man about whom the whole
nation of the Jews, both here and in Jerusalem, have
petitioned me, crying out that he ought not to live any
longer.

"I could not find that he had committed any crime
worthy of the death penalty, and he has now appealed
to Caesar. Therefore, I have determined to send him
to Rome. But I have nothing very definite to write to
the emperor about him. Consequently, I have brought
him before you all, and especially before you, King
Agrippa, in order that, after he has been examined, I may
have something to commit to writing.

"For it seems to me unreasonable to send a prisoner,
and not to specify the charges made against him."

After this introduction by Festus, Agrippa took over
the hearing. He looked very proud and regal, this scion
of the house of Herod, as he sat there among the rich
hangings and elaborate decorations of the audience
chamber, on his golden chair, with his fair sister beside
him.

Yet I could not but recall that his family had often
harried and persecuted our faith. His father had beheaded
James, the brother of John, and cast Peter into prison.
Another member of his family, Antipas, had imprisoned
and beheaded John the Baptist, and had mocked and
scourged our Lord Jesus Christ. The common ancestor
of them all, Herod the Great, had sought to slay the infant Jesus. Christians had indeed learned to dread the
name of Herod.

As for Agrippa's sister Bernice, who sat beside him,

she was not of a sort to inspire confidence in Christians. It was rumored that she was interested in our doctrines, and it may have been that her sister Drusilla, who had so recently listened to me at Caesarea, had told her something about me.

But Bernice had those same traits of viciousness that marred the lives of other members of her family, such as Herodias and Salome. She was first married to her uncle, Herod of Chalcis, but after his death she returned to live with her brother Agrippa, some said in criminal intimacy. She then married Polemo, King of Pontus, who became a Jew that he might win her hand. But Bernice shortly left him, and returned to live again with her brother.

It was before such a pair that I was brought to answer for my faith.

When Agrippa took over the proceedings in the audience chamber, he said to me,

"Paul, you may speak for yourself."

I spoke as follows:

"I consider myself fortunate, King Agrippa, to answer here in your presence to all the accusations of the Jews, because I know that you are expert in all the customs and beliefs of this people. Therefore, I pray you, hear me patiently.

"All the Jews know my manner of life from my youth onward, how I lived among my own people at Jerusalem. They who knew me from the beginning could tell, if they would testify, how I lived the life of a Pharisee, the strictest sect of our religion.

"Yet now I stand here and am judged because I have hope in the promise which God made to our forefathers, namely, the promise of the resurrection; the same promise which our twelve tribes, constantly serving God day and night, hope to have fulfilled for them. For this hope's sake, King Agrippa, I am accused by the Jews! Why should it be thought incredible that God should raise the dead?

"I once believed that I ought to do many things to oppose the name of Jesus of Nazareth. Such things I did in Jerusalem. Many of God's people did I shut up in prison, having received from the chief priests authority to do so; and when they were put to death, I cast my vote against them.

"I punished them often in every synagogue, and compelled them to blaspheme; and being exceedingly enraged against them, I persecuted them even into distant cities.

"As I went to Damascus upon such a mission, armed with authority from the chief priests, I saw at midday on the road, O king, a light from heaven, brighter than the brightness of the sun, shining round about me and those who journeyed with me. And when we had all fallen to the earth, I heard a voice speaking to me, and saying in the Hebrew tongue, 'Saul, Saul, why do you persecute me? It is hard for you to fight against that which you know to be the right.'

" 'Who are you, my Lord?' I asked.

" 'I am Jesus, whom you are persecuting,' came the answer. 'But rise, stand up, for I have appeared to you in order to make you my minister, and my witness both as to these things which you have seen, and those things in which I will appear to you; delivering you both from the Jews and from the Gentiles, to whom I now send you, to open their eyes, and to turn them from darkness to light, and from the power of Satan to God, that they may receive forgiveness for their sins, and an inheritance among those who are made holy through faith in me.'

"Therefore, O King Agrippa, I was not disobedient to the heavenly vision; but undertook to show first to the people in Damascus and at Jerusalem, and throughout all Judea, and then to the Gentiles, that they should repent and turn to God, and do works appropriate to their repentance.

"For these reasons, the Jews caught me in the temple, and tried to kill me. But having obtained help from God, I continue to this day, bearing witness of this Truth to both small and great, and saying nothing but what the prophets and Moses have said should come to pass: that Jesus should suffer, and that he should be the first to rise from the dead, and should thus bring light to the Jews and to the Gentiles."

Here I was interrupted by Festus, who found it hard to comprehend what I was saying, and thought I was losing my reason.

"Paul, Paul," he cried with a loud voice, "you are beside yourself! Much learning is driving you mad."

"Most noble Festus," I reassured him, "I am not mad, but am speaking forth words of truth and soberness. For the King knows about these things, and before him I

speak freely. I am sure that none of these things are
unknown to him, for all this did not happen in secret.
King Agrippa, do you believe the prophets? I know that
you believe."

Then Agrippa said to me,

"You almost persuade me to be a Christian."

"I would to God," said I to him, "that not only you,
but all that hear me this day, were such as I am—except
for these chains."

And I held up my arms, which had chains upon them,
binding me to the guards that stood beside me.

When I had finished speaking, Festus, the King, Bernice, the dignitaries and all present stood up, and the
chief among them withdrew to deliberate on my case.

"This man is doing nothing which deserves death or
imprisonment," I heard them say among themselves.

Finally King Agrippa turned to Festus and said openly,

"This man might have been set at liberty, if he had
not appealed to Caesar."

But I had appealed, and now there was nothing for
me to do but remain in custody at Caesarea until I
could be sent under guard on the long voyage to Rome.

Had I been mistaken in appealing my case? Some
doubts assailed me then, and have done so at intervals
ever since. By appealing, I subjected myself to long imprisonment and much hardship. Yet if I had not made
this appeal, when I was first tried by Festus, I might
have been handed over to the harsh injustice of the Jews,
or even murdered by them in some undiscovered ambush

As long as I was in Roman custody, I was at least safe from the assassin's dagger. The prospect of going to Rome, even to be tried, was not entirely unpleasant. For I had long wished to visit that city, and to meet the disciples there, with whom I had been in correspondence. And if the Roman law could be depended upon to maintain its high reputation for justice and fairness, surely the emperor's court at Rome would set me free.

Along with other prisoners on their way to Rome to be tried, I was delivered into the custody of one Julius, a centurion or captain in the Augustan cohort of the Roman army.

The necessary arrangements being made, we went aboard a ship in the harbor of Caesarea and began our adventurous voyage to Rome. With me as companions went Luke and another fellow-Christian, Aristarchus the Macedonian, from Thessalonica.

Sixteen

——

O^UR SHIP was bound for its home port in the province of Asia. We planned to transfer from it, in any port where we could find suitable shipping, to a vessel bound for Rome.

First of our ports of call was Sidon, and here the centurion Julius showed great kindness to me, by permitting me to visit friends ashore to refresh myself.

Thence we sailed to Myra, a seaport in Lycia. And here a surprise awaited me.

Thekla, whom I had not seen for years, appeared to greet me, accompanied by a group of followers who had attached themselves to her in her travels. She had been seeking me for many months, she said.

The centurion allowed me to go ashore here, as in Sidon, and I took Thekla and some of her followers with me to the house of one of the Christians in Myra. There she told me of her continued growth in power and understanding since we had last met at Antioch, long ago, when I had left her, sadly distraught, in the care of kindly women.

She desired, she said, to return to her home in Iconium, where we had first met, and I encouraged her to go there. Her condition was much improved since I had last seen her, and I rejoiced in her progress.

"Go, and teach the word of God," I told her.

With great affection she bade me farewell, throwing herself at my feet and covering me with kisses. Then, gathering her little following around her, she took the road for Iconium.

Word has come to me of her from time to time. She stayed for a certain period at Iconium, going often, I am told, to the house where she first came to see me, and there giving thanks to God for the Truth that I had imparted to her. She also comforted her old mother, who was reconciled to her after many years of separation.

Later, she went to Seleucia, and lived in a grotto outside the city, becoming widely known throughout the countryside for her wisdom and for her skill in the healing art. The sick were brought to her from all the region round about, and cured of their distresses.

A tale is told that the physicians of Seleucia, having lost their trade because of her skill in healing, conspired against her. They sent a gang of ruffians to assault her in her grotto, but she, sensing their design, and guided by divine revelation, withdrew into the crevice of a great rock, which closed about her and shielded her from their attack.

More recently I have heard that she desires to come
to Rome to see me. I await her coming, but she has not
come. Farewell, dear Thekla, if I should not see you
more. We have not labored in vain. Many have been
blessed by our ministrations. And though we have met
but seldom, there has been between us such a companionship as comes to few.

A strange fellowship this, a companionship in absence.
Mine has been a lonely road, and a rough one. There has
been no place along its course for womankind. Yet could
there have been such a place, yours would have been the
sort of faith that would have filled it.

Hail, Thekla, and farewell. May God attend your
every thought and deed. We are together in the Holy
Spirit.

*   *   *

At Myra we found a large Egyptian grain ship, bound
for Italy. The centurion Julius had me, my fellow prisoners and companions go aboard.

Then began a long and eventful voyage. It was tedious
at first, for we encountered unfavorable winds and made
little progress, spending many days in sailing slowly as
far as Cnidus and the island of Crete. We finally dropped
anchor at a place called Fair Havens, near the city of
Laesa, on the southern coast of Crete. The season was
by this time far advanced and that time of the year was
approaching when it was considered unsafe to venture
into the open sea.

As I prayed and pondered upon our position, it seemed

unwise to me to venture out into the Mediterranean at this time. I therefore addressed myself to Julius, to the master of the ship, and to its owner, who happened to be aboard for this voyage.

"Sirs," said I, "I perceive that this voyage will result in much loss and damage, not only to the ship and its cargo, but even to the lives of those aboard."

But the master and the owner of the ship would not listen to my warning, and Julius, although inclined to pay attention, overruled my objections. After all, I was only a prisoner aboard the vessel, although Julius and some others were very kind to me, and inclined to give much weight to what I said.

It was decided, since the anchorage where we lay was not convenient for wintering in, that we should sail to Phoenix, a harbor farther west along the coast of Crete, which is sheltered from the southwest and northwest winds. When a gentle south wind sprang up, they felt certain that they could carry out this plan, and we weighed anchor and sailed westward along the shore of Crete.

But not long afterwards, a tempestuous northeast wind arose, sweeping down from the mountains of Crete, struck the ship violently and sent her out of control. All that could be done was to let her run before the gale.

The wind drove us toward Clauda, about twenty miles to the southwest. Running under the lee of this island, the sailors had barely enough time to hoist aboard the boat that had been trailing at our stern, and to undergird the ship to strengthen her. They did this with tackle that was carried for such emergencies, by passing ropes under the keel and over the gunwales and drawing them tight by means of pulleys and levers, to prevent planks and timbers from working.

We feared the ship might be driven into the Syrtis, a notoriously dangerous bay on the coast of Africa.

Being greatly tossed about by the tempest, we began next day to lighten the ship by throwing overboard whatever could be spared. On the third day, passengers and sailors joined in casting out all the spare gear of the ship.

Then for many days neither sun nor stars appeared, and we knew not where we were. No small tempest lay upon us, and all hope that we should be saved deserted many of those aboard.

I fasted and prayed continually, and finally a vision came to me, which I shared with all upon the ship, standing in the midst of them and saying,

"Sirs, you should have listened to me, and not set sail from Crete. Then you would have been spared this suffering and loss. But be of good cheer, for no man among you shall lose his life, but only the ship shall be lost. For there stood beside me last night an angel of that God to whom I belong, and whom I serve.

"And the angel said, 'Fear not, Paul, for you must be brought before Caesar; and behold, God has granted you the lives of all them that sail with you.'

"Therefore, sirs, I believe God, and that everything shall be exactly as it was told me. Nevertheless, we shall be cast upon a certain island."

Fourteen long days passed. Then, at midnight, while

we were being buffeted about in stormy waters, the seamen—thinking they heard the sound of breakers ahead—concluded that we were drawing near to some shore. The ship's officers took soundings, and found the depth to be twenty fathoms. When we had gone a little farther, they took soundings again, and found fifteen fathoms.

Fearing that we might be driven upon rocks, they let go four anchors by the stern, and waited anxiously for daylight, to run the ship ashore.

Fear overcame some of the sailors at this crucial moment, and they plotted to save themselves, leaving the ship and its passengers to their fate.

They let the ship's boat down into the water, saying that they were going to carry out some anchors from the bow. But I detected their deception before they had been able to carry it out.

Calling Julius and his soldiers just as the sailors were preparing to go over the side, I said to them,

"Unless these men stay in the ship, you cannot be saved."

Then the soldiers cut the ropes of the ship's boat and let her fall off. Thus was treachery forestalled, and the fulfillment of prophecy made possible.

As dawn approached, I tried to comfort all those aboard, to calm them and to encourage them in normal ways of thought and action. Many had not eaten for days, and I urged them to take some food.

"This is the fourteenth day that you have waited anxiously, and have fasted and eaten little or nothing," said

I to them. "Therefore, I pray you, take some food. This is essential for your well-being. Not a hair is going to perish from the head of any one of you."

Having spoken thus, I took bread and gave thanks to God in the presence of them all. And when I had broken the bread, I began to eat. This cheered them, and they also took some food. Altogether, there were 276 persons in the ship.

When they had eaten enough, they lightened the ship further by throwing the cargo of wheat into the sea.

Day was now dawning, but the shore in front of us was not familiar to anyone aboard. An inlet with a sandy beach could be seen, and it was decided, if possible, to run the ship into it.

The anchors were cut adrift, the lashings of the rudders were unloosed, the foresail was hoisted, and the ship made for the shore. But she ran into a place where two currents crossed, and there was nothing to do but run her aground. The bow stuck fast on the shore, and remained unmovable, but the stern was broken up by the violence of the waves.

The soldiers, fearing that we prisoners would swim ashore and escape, urged that we all should be put to death. But the centurion, Julius, who desired to save my life, kept them from carrying out their purpose. He commanded that those who could swim should first cast themselves into the sea, and get to land, and that the rest should then follow, some on planks, and some on wreckage from the ship. In this way, we all escaped safely to land.

On reaching shore, we learned that the island where we were was Malta. I gave thanks for our deliverance, and others joined with me in my thanksgiving.

Some of the natives of the island, who spoke a language different from our own, appeared and showed us no little kindness. They kindled a fire, and received us every one, drenched and exhausted as we were. It was raining steadily, and very cold.

I gathered a bundle of sticks and laid them on the fire, when suddenly a viper darted out of the heat, and seized upon my hand. When the natives saw the creature hanging onto my hand, they said among themselves,

"Beyond doubt this man is a murderer; though he has escaped the sea, yet unerring justice will not permit him to live."

I shook off the beast into the fire, and felt no harm. They expected me to swell with inflammation, or suddenly fall down dead. But after they had watched me for a while, and saw that no harm had come to me, they changed their minds, and began to say that I was a god.

Not far from the place where we landed were estates belonging to the governor of the island, whose name was Publius. He received us into his house, and courteously entertained us for three days.

Publius' father was ill of dysentery, and suffered from attacks of fever. I went to see him, and prayed for him, and laid my hands upon him, and healed him of his sickness. After this, others in the island who had diseases came and were healed. They showered us with gifts and, when the time came to depart, three months later, they loaded us down with everything we needed.

We finally sailed away in a grain ship from Alexandria, which had wintered at the island. She was called the Castor and Pollux, after the hero-patrons of Roman sailors, and on her prow she had the figures of these two supposed benefactors of sea-faring men.

Putting for three days into Syracuse, in Sicily, we then sailed on to Rhegium, which lies at the toe of the boot formed by the Italian peninsula, and there waited another day for favorable weather to pass through the straits of Messina. Then a south wind sprung up and carried us through these narrow waters, and on up the coast of Italy.

On our left, as we sailed, we saw a conical island which rose abruptly from the sea and sent forth a column of smoke from its apex; they told us it was the volcanic isle of Stromboli.

Next morning we entered the beautiful bay of Naples, and knew that our voyage was nearly at an end. Another cone-shaped mountain, Vesuvius, towered above the bay, its seaward slopes covered with vineyards. It is hard for me to believe that a countryside which was so placid on that day has since been transformed into a scene of desolation and destruction by the great eruption of this volcano.

Sailing across this glorious bay into its northern portion, we were met on every hand, as we approached the port of Puteoli,* by reminders of the magnificence of the Caesars.

In our wake lay the isle of Capri, where the vicious Tiberius—master of the world when our Lord was crucified—had lived a life of shameless profligacy, surrounded by a swarm of sinful parasites.

I noted that our vessel, on entering the bay between Capri and the promontory of Minerva, did not strike its topsails, as did other ships that entered. An aged mariner aboard our ship explained the reason.

"It was the great emperor Augustus," said he, "who recognized the importance of the trade between Alexandria and Puteoli, and as a result of this our Egyptian vessels enjoy special favors here.

"Caesar Augustus happened one day to be cruising these fair waters in his yacht, when one of our grain ships passed close by. Members of the crew recognized the emperor, and brought forth garlands and incense that they might pay him the divine honors due to the great man-god, Caesar.

" 'By your providence, O Augustus,' they cried, 'are our voyages made safe and our trade prosperous!'

"The emperor was so pleased with this tribute that he distributed a large sum of gold among his suite, on condition that all of it be spent for goods from Alexandria. And ever since that time, we have had special favors in this great port."

Reminders of still another Caesar stood close at hand.

* Modern Pozzuoli.

There in the shallow waters of an inlet were the remnants of the fantastic and useless bridge thrown across the bay, at vast expense, by the mad emperor Caligula, in order that he might drive his chariot across it in simulation of a conquering hero.

And there, close beside the fashionable seaside resort of Baiae, beyond the brightly-colored sails of Roman pleasure-boats, was Bauli, where the reigning emperor, Nero, who now holds me in bonds, had only two years before plotted the murder of his own mother, Agrippina.

One could not come into the port of Puteoli without being very conscious of the Caesars—and of the vicious lives that most of them led, and of the luxury-laden corruption of their courtiers. Here were the oyster-beds that supplied the rich tables of the Roman nobles. Here were the ships that brought the wealth of all the world to the imperial city. Here, at anchor, was one of the war-fleets that made the seas subservient to Rome. Here, in the midst of riches, were the throngs of poor and hungry, who crowded the wharves as we approached, welcoming the arrival of a cargo of grain from Egypt.

Christian brothers who had heard of our coming greeted us as we went ashore. They took us into their homes and desired us to stay with them seven days. The good centurion Julius granted us permission, and thus we first preached the Word of God on the Italian mainland at Puteoli, at our voyage's end.

Hence by the Campanian Way we were led on to Capua, where we took the Appian Way northwestward

toward Rome. These great highways teemed with travelers. There were many who went on foot, and others
who rode in vehicles, or on horseback. Conveyances such
as I had not seen before, but only heard of, were common here, on the roads leading into the world's metropolis.

Slaves carrying palanquins hurried their masters, or
their ladies, along the road to city or to seaport. Now
and again a light horse-drawn cabriolet, or *cisium*,
dashed by, carrying some gay young noble to his pleas-
ure-craft in the harbor at Baiae. Or a more ponderous
four-wheeled carriage, called a *rheda*, transported a whole
family on its way. Occasionally we met a company of
soldiers on the march. The vigorous, bustling life of the
metropolis flowed out along the Appian Way to meet us.

On we went, beside the seashore or through long,
low stretches where the highway led straight and white,
like an endless bridge, across the marshes. It was at such
a place as this, at the end of a canal that had bordered
the road for twenty miles, at a place called Appii Forum,
that we were first met and welcomed by some of the disciples from the church in Rome. Ten miles farther on,
at Three Taverns, another group awaited us.

When I saw these faithful ones, who came bravely
and joyously out to meet a prisoner, I thanked God, and
took courage.

The road seemed easier now, and my chains lighter.
As the highway led us over the southern slopes of the
Alban Hills, my feet took wings with the joy and grati-

tude I felt toward these loving ones who had come to greet me. Through towns and villages, and over lofty viaducts we passed, until, from the summit of a rise, I caught my first glimpse of the city—Rome.

Seventeen

—

T<small>HIS</small> enormous city of some two million persons, spread across the broad campagna before me, was such a sight as I had never seen. Many rich and beautiful cities had I visited, but none so vast, so overpowering, as this. In a grand panorama, it extended from below the place where I stood to the blue Sabine Mountains on the right, and across a seemingly unending vista of hills and plain, an almost unbroken expanse of houses, gardens, temples, walls, aqueducts and roads.

Never have I forgotten the impact of that view. Here was the heart, the capital, of that Gentile world which it was my charge to bring into the fold of the Great Shepherd.

Descending from the Alban Hills, we struck across the plain. Gradually the city grew up about us. The houses were closer together, the road became ever more crowded. We had not yet reached the ramparts, but the city was all around us, having overflowed the confining limits of the wall of Servius Tullus.

Finally we entered the city proper by the Porta Capena, dripping with water from the aqueduct that passed over it, and went along the Sacra Via to the Forum. Here was the Golden Milestone, where the great highways from all the provinces converged, the very center of the empire.

Stately buildings: temples, monuments, palaces, stood on very hand. In front of me rose the famed Capitoline Hill, and on my left the Palatine Hill, covered by the buildings of the imperial palace, the House of Caesar. To one of these buildings I was led, along with my fellow prisoners. The good centurion, Julius, presented his credentials to Burrus, the prefect of the pretorian guard, whose duty it was to keep in custody all accused persons who were to be tried before the emperor. And having thus, at last, discharged his duty, Julius took his leave; not, I thought, without regret, for he had become attached to us as we to him, through trials and hardships endured together.

Burrus, who at this time was perhaps the most influential official next to the emperor himself, decreed that I should not be shut up in a prison cell, but that I might dwell in a house to myself, with, of course, a soldier always present to guard me. Although confined to my house, and chained day and night by one arm to a soldier of the pretorian guard, I was nevertheless permitted to see anyone I wished to send for, and allowed many comforts which the disciples hastened to provide for me.

There was a large and prosperous community of Jews in Rome, who lived in a district across the Tiber from the main part of the city. They enjoyed a large measure of freedom from persecution at this time, in contrast to their position under the emperor Claudius, who had caused them to be expelled from the city.

The Christians in Rome were likewise comparatively free from oppression in these years. Many Romans did not distinguish between Christians and Jews, but thought of us still as a sect of the Hebrews. The difference between our creed and that of the Jews was not yet so clear in Italy as it had become in Palestine and elsewhere.

Since I found myself a prisoner on complaint of the Jews, it seemed wise to communicate with the Jewish colony here to discover whether they were as bitter against me as their co-religionists of Jerusalem. Three days after my arrival in Rome, I sent for the leaders of their community, and they assembled at my house.

"Brothers," said I, as soon as they had gathered there, "though I have done nothing against our people, or the customs of our forefathers, I was handed over as a prisoner from Jerusalem into the hands of the Romans. They, when they had examined me, would have let me go, because they found me not guilty of any offense punishable by death. But when the Jews objected to the Roman decision, I was obliged to appeal to Caesar; not, however, because I had any accusation to make against my people.

"For this reason I have sent for you, to see you and

to speak to you: I am bound with this chain because I believe in him who is the hope of Israel."

And I lifted my arm to show them the chain that bound me to my guard.

They disclaimed any knowledge of my case.

"We have neither received letters from Judea about you," they declared, "nor have any of our brothers who have come here from Jerusalem spoken nor proved anything against you. But we should be glad to hear from you what it is that you believe, for we know that this sect is everywhere spoken against."

It was evident from this that my accusers had not yet arrived in Rome, nor pleaded their case against me.

We fixed a day when the Jews should return to my house to hear more of what I had to say, and when the time arrived, they and many others came to hear me.

To them I explained the meaning of the kingdom of God, and endeavored from morning to evening to persuade them of the truth about Jesus, basing my arguments both on the law of Moses and on the writings of the prophets.

Some believed the things I said, and others did not. As they disagreed among themselves, I said to them, just before they departed,

"Right well did the Holy Spirit say to our forefathers through the prophet Isaiah: 'Go to this people and say, "You shall hear, and not understand; and see, but not perceive; for the heart of this people has grown callous, and they are dull of hearing, and they have closed their eyes; for fear that they might see, and hear, and understand, and be converted, and I should heal them." '

"Therefore be it known to you," I told these Jews of Rome, "that the salvation of God has now been sent to the Gentiles, and they will give heed to it."

After I had said this, they took their leave, discussing furiously among themselves.

*   *   *

The Roman courts required that no case could be brought before them without the prosecutor appearing in person. As my accusers had not yet arrived, my case dragged on. According to Roman law, the prosecutor on a criminal charge was not the State, but any private individual who chose to bring a charge.

Eventually I was formally accused on three counts: first, with causing factious disturbances among Jews throughout the empire, which was an offense against the Roman government and amounted to treason against the emperor; second, with being a ringleader of the sect of the Nazarenes, which involved heresy against the law of Moses; and third, with an attempt to profane the temple at Jerusalem. This last was an offense not only against the Jewish, but also against the Roman law, which protected the Jews in the exercise of their religion.

My accusers had to bring their witnesses from widely separate areas, and this took time. Also, Nero's regulations required that prosecutors and accused with their witnesses must be heard on each charge separately and sentence pronounced on the first charge before the second was taken up.

As a result of all these legal technicalities, the case against me lagged interminably, through a series of hearings and adjournments.

For two whole years I continued under guard in my own house. But I did not let this confinement prevent me from carrying on my holy work.

No obstacle was placed in the way of those who wished to come to see me, and many came. To them I preached the kingdom of God, and taught concerning the Lord Jesus Christ with full confidence, and no one forbade me.

People from many different nations who happened to be in Rome, and who heard of my teaching, came and were converted. Some among these were from lands so far afield as Spain and Britain. Thus the church of God spread from the house of my confinement to even the farthest corners of the world.

Some of my good friends continued with me most of the time. Among them were Luke, Timothy, Tychicus, and Mark—whom I forgave his youthful lapses, and who was a constant source of comfort to me—and Aristarchus the Macedonian from Thessalonica, and Epaphras from Colossae, and Epaphroditus from Philippi, and Andronicus and Junias. These faithful ones rallied from many lands and cities to cheer me in my time of need.

There was also the fugitive slave, Onesimus. This poor man came to me one day and confessed that he had belonged to a prominent Christian named Philemon, of Colossae in Phrygia, in whose house the church in that city was accustomed to meet. Onesimus had robbed his master, fled from Colossae, and after many hardships found his way to Rome. Here he had lived in squalor among the vicious mob that crowded the lower quarters of the city.

Yet he had heard of me and of my teaching, and finally gained the courage to come and tell me his story. So deep was his contrition, and so earnest his desire to reform his ways, that I took him to my heart. Gladly would I have kept him by me as a servant and companion.

But this I could not do so long as his debt to his former master, Philemon, remained unpaid.

It happened that just at this time I had written a letter to the church at Colossae,* and was sending it by the hand of Tychicus. Nothing could have been more opportune than to send Onesimus with him, bearing a letter to Philemon,† in that same city. This I did.

My letter to Philemon was prompted not only by my affection for Onesimus, but by the need, so evident to me, of improving the relations between masters and slaves. The utmost cruelty was practiced by many masters, and the result was smoldering hatred, with occasional outbursts of revolt and murder by the slaves.

There had been a terrible example of this at Rome, even since my arrival there. The prefect of the city, Pedanius Secundus, had been murdered by one of his slaves. As punishment, the whole body of slaves belonging to the prefect, numbering hundreds, and including women

* The Epistle to the Colossians.
† The Epistle to Philemon.

and children, were executed in a body, although no suspicion of guilt attached to more than a handful of them.

In my letter to Philemon, I tried to breathe into the relationship between owner and slave something of the love of Christ. I offered to pay what Onesimus owed him, and asked that, if he could spare Onesimus, he would permit him to return and serve me. For, as I pointed out, the name Onesimus means "useful," and I would that the man might be useful to me as well as to his master. Also, I asked Philemon to pray for me, that I might be liberated and come to visit the church in Colossae.

Onesimus set off joyfully, bearing the letter to Philemon, at the moment that Tychicus took the same course with my letter to the Colossians.

In this latter epistle I tried to correct certain evils which, I had learned, were springing up in the church at Colossae. Epaphras, the founder of that church, was with me at Rome and had told me of these dangers.

Certain heretics there were teaching the people to worship a hierarchy of angels, and seeking to substitute for our faith a system of mystic philosophy, which the people of Phrygia were in general prone to adopt. Therefore I warned the Colossians:

"Take care lest anyone captivate you with philosophy and vain deceit, according to human traditions and the world's crude notions, instead of according to Christ. For it is in Christ that God's full nature dwells embodied, and it is in him that you are made whole."

This and other warnings it seemed wise to send them,

along with commendation for their faithfulness and encouragement to higher achievements.

Other letters to the churches were the fruit of my long detention at Rome, while the preliminaries of my trial were slowly being carried through. Visitors from churches in many cities came to see me in the house where I was detained. Often they brought news of importance, that led me to write an epistle to the congregation concerned.

Sometimes I dictated these letters to a scribe, usually the good Tertius, who has always been ready and willing to aid me in this regard. To such letters I often added a conclusion and signature in my own handwriting, to assure the brothers of their genuineness. And sometimes, I have written whole letters myself, seated at a table with my guard beside me, resting the heavy chain that links me to him on the table before us, and tracing the uncial characters with my reed pen upon the Egyptian papyrus in black ink, all with my own hand.

Among the epistles which I wrote at this time was a circular letter to several of the churches in Asia, and especially to the Laodiceans; this letter was carried by Tychicus on the same journey when he conveyed my epistle to the Colossians.*

In this letter I counseled purity of life and steadfastness in the faith. And, as I wrote in the presence of a member of the pretorian guard, and was daily in touch

---

* This is the letter now known as the Epistle to the Ephesians. Most scholars are convinced that it was not originally addressed to the church at Ephesus.

with the affairs of soldiers, I likened the Christian's armament to the arms of the military man.

"Put on the whole armor of God," I wrote, "that you may be able to stand firm in the day of battle and, having fought to the end, remain victor on the field.

"Stand, therefore, having bound about you the girdle of Truth, and having donned the breastplate of righteousness; above all, holding the shield of faith, which enables you to quench all the fiery darts of the wicked; and crowned with the helmet of salvation, and wearing on your feet the shoes of the gospel of peace; and wielding the sword of the Spirit, which is the Word of God."

*   *   *

Hardly had Tychicus set off with these letters, when a messenger from a different quarter led me to indite still another epistle.

Epaphroditus, one of the leading elders of the church at Philippi, arrived at Rome, bringing an offering in my behalf from the members of that church. I was deeply touched by this evidence of affection from a church that I have always dearly loved. It was at Philippi that I first preached the Word in Europe, and there that Silas and I were delivered from prison by the earthquake, and baptized the jailer and his household.

The brave Christians of Philippi have always upheld the faith, and often have stood as a shining light when others have been dimmed.

Epaphroditus, who brought the offering, was taken

very ill, and many prayers were said for him by all of
us before he was again restored, and able to carry back
to them at Philippi my commendations and my thanks.
When he was well again, I sent him home with my
letter.*

There was little to rebuke in the church at Philippi.
Two women of the congregation had been quarreling;
therefore I besought these two, Euodias and Syntyche,
to be of the same Mind. But for the most part, my epistle was one of gratitude for the help I had received from
the Philippians on more than one occasion; a warning
against evils, and an exhortation to continue in the good
life.

"Brothers," I wrote to them, "I do not claim that I
have yet laid hold of the prize, but this one thing I do:
forgetting those things which lie behind me, and reaching forward to those things which lie ahead, I press onward toward the goal and the reward of the high calling
of God in Christ Jesus."

If it seems strange to any reader that I employed the
language of the race track and the athletic games, let me
explain that I have found it wise, even as our Lord spoke
in parables, to clothe my messages in words that the
simplest of our people may readily understand.

Once I was at Corinth when the great Isthmian Games
were held. There I saw the runners contending in the
races, straining to win from the hands of the judges the
chaplet of pine that was the prize of the victor. I learned

* The Epistle to the Philippians.

of the careful training that each contestant underwent, the temperance and self-restraint that were imposed upon them all. And I have often thought of myself as a runner in such a race, striving to win the priceless goal of salvation.

In these terms, therefore, I have spoken and written to the disciples, in the assurance that I shall be understood. For the idiom of the games is known and spoken among all classes, and in all the cities of the empire.

Likewise, have I written in terms of soldiery. My lot has been cast, especially here at Rome, among these hardy men at arms. One by one, the men of the pretorian guard have been assigned to guard me. In the enforced intimacy of my detention, I have come to know them all. From them I have learned what was happening in the imperial palace and in the city. Through them I have come to know many members of the imperial household, from humble slaves to high officials. They all know me as a prisoner for the cause of Christ, and some have been converted.

Many of these soldiers are rough, cruel men, but some have been touched by my teaching. When the disciples have come to meet and pray with me, it is a strange sight to see the gentleness and meekness of their natures, in contrast with the stern visages of my guards. Here in the very shadow of Nero's palace, where luxury and vice are rampant, some of the emperor's retainers have learned a purer, better way of life.

*   *   *

As the weeks and months of my waiting dragged on, the numbers of the faithful steadily increased. They often brought me word of events that seemed to favor or to endanger my case. In constant prayer, I awaited the time of my trial before Nero.

Eighteen

As THE day approached when I must appear before the imperial court, certain events transpired which seemed to make my situation more precarious than ever before.

First of these was the death of the pretorian prefect, Burrus, who had been so kind in permitting me to live in my own house under guard, not confined to one of the public prisons. It had been a comfort to me to recall that this man, who seemed to have taken a kindly interest in my welfare, was in a position of unsurpassed power as an adviser of the emperor.

After his death, his office was divided between two commissioners, Fenius Rufus and Sofonius Tigellinus. The former was a respectable man, but of no great force of character; the latter was extremely ambitious and unscrupulous, and one of Nero's most unprincipled favorites.

I had nothing in particular to fear from the new commissioners, yet I felt that my position was less secure than when the good Burrus had been in office.

Much worse than this change, from my point of view, was the rise to power of Nero's adulterous mistress, Poppaea, whom he married about this time. She had become a proselyte to Judaism, and her friendship for the high priest's party at Jerusalem seemed an ill omen for my safety. She had almost unbounded control over Nero, and I well knew that if a whim overtook her to ask for my head, she could have it in a moment.

This terrible creature had persuaded Nero to divorce his young wife, Octavia, and then to murder her. She even had the head of her poor victim sent to her from Pandataria, so that she might gloat over it.

Making her hold on the emperor even stronger, she gave birth at this moment to a child, a daughter, with the result that Nero caused temples to be erected in honor of her and the infant, and ordered them to be worshiped as divine.

She was on the most friendly terms with my most bitter enemies, the Jews of Jerusalem, having interceded with the emperor on their behalf in a dispute which arose between them and King Herod Agrippa II. Agrippa had built a high tower beside the temple at Jerusalem and delighted to annoy the Jews by peering down from it into the inner courts, and observing all that went on there.

The Jews considered this a bold invasion of their privacy. They built a high wall at the side of the temple

enclosure to shut off Agrippa's view. He ordered them
to tear down the wall. They refused, and appealed to
Caesar for support against the king's command. Poppaea
interceded for the Jews, and the wall was allowed to
stand.

It was not comfortable to think that this woman,
whom the Jews might have informed against me, could
gain her slightest wish from the powerful ruler who was
to decide my fate. For the first time, it began to appear
that my trial might have a tragic outcome.

I urged the Christians of Rome to redouble their
prayers for me, and they rushed to my aid and comfort.

At last the day set for the trial arrived. I was led by
my guards out of my house and up to the imperial palace on the Palatine Hill. There, I was taken into a vast
audience chamber, its walls faced with beautiful and precious marbles from the quarries of Egypt and Libya. The
lofty ceiling was painted to represent the starry sky, because it had been the tradition in earlier and simpler
days for Roman magistrates to hold their hearings in the
open air.

At the far end of the hall, on a dais, sat the emperor.
Here was that Nero who ruled the world, whose private
life was the scandal of his people, yet whose name re-
sounded throughout all nations as the most powerful of
monarchs. Here was the man who, having murdered his
mother, his wife and his adopted brother, still sat upon
a throne.

A man of rather less than average stature, his features
were sharp and inquisitive. He was about 25 years of

age, according to my reckoning, but his years of sin sat
heavily upon him. His flowing purple robes, gold-en-
crusted, seemed to weigh him down, as something more
substantial than he was himself.

Here was an emperor who, although the heir of all
the dignity of the vastest empire, nevertheless chose to
disport himself in the public theater as a musician, and
to compete with professionals in the circus as a chariot-
eer.

Seated in a semicircle behind the emperor were his
council of assessors. There were twenty of them, including the two Consuls, the leading magistrates of Rome,
and a number of Senators, chosen by lot. Their func-
tion was to advise him on points of law, but they had no
power, and he was independent of them in rendering
judgment.

My guards led me, in chains, the full length of this
spacious chamber, and halted me in front of Nero. The
officers of the court called for order, recited the formula
for opening the proceedings, and the emperor signaled
with his hand that the hearing might commence.

I was not fearful nor abashed, even before so mighty
a tribunal. The only court which could pass sentence
upon me, I knew, was God's own tribunal. Even this
bloodstained emperor could be restrained from injustice
by his will.

The hearing opened with a long speech by the prosecutor, a skillful pleader whom the Jews had hired to
press their charges against me. When he had finished,

and after a short recess of the court, he summoned witnesses to support his accusations.

These were a mixed crew of spies, informers and vaga-
bonds gathered from many different cities, from Jerusalem, Ephesus, Corinth and elsewhere. They made the
most extreme charges, without an element of truth, and
tried to prove the prosecutor's contention that I was the
ringleader of a dangerous sect which plotted against the
empire, and that I was therefore guilty of treason and
deserving of the penalty of death.

The emperor seemed listless as the depositions continued. He longed, no doubt, to be practicing on his
fiddle, or exercising his horses for a chariot race. The
assessors showed varying degrees of interest, but it was
clear that the subtleties of the Jewish law were mystify-
ing to them.

The Jews' pleader was wordy, and his witnesses needed
constant coaching. The emperor at last grew tired and
gave notice that the hearing was ended for the day. He
departed in a flourish of trumpets, and the assessors
trailed wearily out of the judgment hall. I was led away
to my house, to await the next day's session.

The hearing was resumed next morning in the same
setting. The emperor seemed eager to get the business
over. The prosecutor went on with his vague accusations, and brought in new agents of the Sanhedrin to
support him in his claims.

"This man, O Caesar," he finally concluded, "is a dangerous leader of the sect of the Nazarenes. Throughout
the empire, in our synagogues and in the meeting-places

of his followers, he has plotted to overthrow the divinely established government of Your Imperial Majesty. On the proven charge of treason, I demand his head."

Nero's fingers twitched unpleasantly. Had Poppaea already filled his mind with poison against me, the alleged enemy of her friends, the Jews?

"The court will hear your defender," said the emperor to me. "Have you an advocate in court?"

"I shall speak for myself, O Caesar," I replied.

"Then speak on," said he.

Whereupon I gave a brief and simple statement of the facts, as I had already given them before Felix, Festus and Agrippa in Caesarea. I denied the baseless allegations of the prosecution's witnesses, and was in many cases able to point out the impossibility of what they claimed to have occurred.

I pointed out to Caesar that no officer of his had ever found me making dangerous speeches, nor inciting the people to revolt, and I demanded for the sect of the Nazarenes—as the prosecutor had described our church —the same protection as was given to the sects of the Pharisees and the Sadducees.

Although I spoke in the Greek tongue, the emperor and his assessors all understood that language, and I had no need of an interpreter.

Warming to my subject, I tried to give these powerful, worldly men—even this dissolute and vicious ruler— some faint glimpse of the peace and blessedness of life in Christ. A hush fell upon them, and they listened as I spoke.

I was able to prove through witnesses taken from among the disciples at Rome, how I had written to them, counseling not insurrection nor revolt, but obedience to the civil law, in these words:

"Pay to every man what is due him: taxes to whom taxes are due; toll to whom toll is due; respect to whom respect is due; and honor to whom honor is due."

"Are these, O Caesar, the words of a disloyal subject?" I asked the emperor. "Are they not rather the words of one who is a loyal Roman citizen?"

I told them the story of Jesus; of his murder by the Jews; of his resurrection; of my conversion; and of my travels in bringing this message, which the Jews had rejected, to the Gentiles.

"And now, O Caesar," I concluded, "my cause is in your hands. I have appealed to you for justice, and justice I am sure I shall receive."

"The hearing is closed," said Nero. "I will receive the opinions of the assessors."

Each of these twenty dignitaries wrote his verdict on a piece of paper, and all were handed to Nero. He hastily glanced through these ballots, then called for a scroll and wrote his judgment on it.

"The quaestor will read the judgment of Caesar," he announced, and handed the scroll to this official, who advanced to receive it.

Everyone in the hall but the emperor stood up. There was complete silence. My guards stood motionless beside me; not so much as a chink of their armor was heard. My arms hung loose at my sides, my chains resting on the pavement at my feet. I consigned my fate to God.

The quaestor took a deep breath and read aloud in a clear voice that echoed through the great hall:

"The prisoner Paul, in reference to the charges laid against him on appeal to Caesar, is found not guilty. His immediate release is ordered. Nero."

I sank to my knees in a prayer of gratitude. The captain of the guard advanced to where I knelt, followed by a smith with some tools and a small anvil. The soldiers to whom my arms were chained unlocked the shackles from their forearms and let them fall clanging to the floor. The smith took each of my arms in turn, and with skillful strokes of hammer and chisel cut off the iron circlets that bound my wrists.

The captain raised his arm in salute, faced about and marched his men down the hall. The emperor arose, the trumpets sounded, and he walked from the room, followed by his assessors.

I remained kneeling where I was, in prayer. Gradually, with the departure of the officials and the spectators, quiet reigned.

After a few moments, I raised my eyes. I was not alone. On either side of me, in a row extending the width of the chamber, knelt my brothers and sisters of the church at Rome, men, women and children, their faces lifted in shining thankfulness to God for my deliverance.

I began to recite that prayer which the Master taught to his disciples. The voices of the congregation joined with mine:

"Our Father which art in heaven,
Hallowed be thy name.
Thy kingdom come.
Thy will be done in earth, as it is in heaven.
Give us this day our daily bread.
And forgive us our debts, as we forgive our debtors.
And lead us not into temptation, but deliver us from
    evil:
For thine is the kingdom, and the power, and the glory,
    for ever. Amen."

The words rose to the starry ceiling, filling this Roman courtroom with a strange new sound, a benediction on the judgment that had just been rendered there.

When the prayer was finished, each of the loved ones present came to me in turn to grasp my hand and give me the kiss of peace. I raised my arms, now free from bonds for the first time in many months, to bless them and caress them.

My joy knew no bounds. I was again free to do the Lord's work in full liberty.

Nineteen

—

No GRASS grew under my feet in Rome. After a few days of fellowship and rejoicing with the disciples there, I was again off on my travels.

There was so much to be done! More than four years in custody had prevented me from visiting the churches, as I should have done had I been free. Now, I set off in haste to greet the brothers, both in cities where I had been before, and in some which I had never seen.

Through Macedonia, greeted by hundreds of familiar faces, and on to Ephesus, to be welcomed by a church that knew me well. Thence to Colossae and Laodicea, where I had never yet gone, but to whose churches I had written, and promised a visit when I should be free.

Then came news of terrible happenings at Rome. Half the vast city had gone up in flames, with Nero fiddling as it burned. But even worse, our Christian brothers there were charged with having set the fire, and Nero in a burst of rage was burning and killing them by hundreds. I could not bear to think of those who had befriended me, suffering such a fate. I woke from sleep at night shuddering at the miseries inflicted upon my loved ones there.

I could not go to Rome to help them. There was nothing I could do but pray. This I did, and with me all the churches.

Rather than remain inactive, stunned by the news from Rome, I undertook the farthest voyage I had yet made, to Spain. Avoiding Italy, I went from Ephesus by way of Marseilles to this farthest western land. There I remained two years, founding churches in many of the cities on the Spanish coast.

Then I returned to Ephesus, in time to combat the teachings of heretics who denied the resurrection of the dead. And when I had to leave Ephesus for Macedonia, I put in charge there my own son in the Spirit, Timothy, a worthy warden of the church.

From Macedonia, I wrote to Timothy a letter * which I thought would strengthen his hand in dealing with the troublous persons who sought to sow dissension in our Ephesian congregation. There were women in the church there who were acting in a manner most unfitting; them I cautioned to be more Christlike

"Fight the good fight of faith," I counseled Timothy. "Lay hold on eternal life, to which you are called, and to which you have testified before many witnesses.

* The First Epistle to Timothy.

"O Timothy, keep that which is committed to your trust, avoiding profane and vain babblings, and controversy falsely called knowledge, in embracing which some of the brethren have wandered from the faith."

Shortly afterwards, I went to Crete, taking with me Titus, whom I left there as my representative. Also to him I wrote a letter from Ephesus, confirming his authority.*

The Cretans had a reputation, even among their own poets and philosophers, of being a beastly, sluggish people. I instructed Titus to rebuke them sharply.

"Unto the pure all things are pure," I wrote to him, "but unto them who are defiled and unbelieving, nothing is pure, but even their mind and conscience is defiled."

I planned to spend the winter at Nicopolis, in Macedonia, and urged Titus to come and join me there.

Visiting first Miletus and then Corinth, I pressed on to Nicopolis, whence I could make excursion to the churches of Illyricum, which were in need of guidance.

But I was not permitted to spend the winter in Nicopolis, as I had planned. For there a plot was sprung upon me. All unexpectedly, I was seized by the Roman authorities, and hurried off to Italy, again in chains.

The policy of Nero's government toward Christians had entirely changed. We were no longer classed with the Jews, and given toleration. We were a proscribed sect, accused of having burned the imperial city.

I was treated much more harshly than at the time of

* The Epistle to Titus.

my former imprisonment. My chains were heavier, my guard more strict, my quarters in Rome more confined, and with fewer liberties.

Most of my friends had perished or fled in terror before I was seized; few dared to come to see me in my prison. My trial was held without delay.

This time I was brought not before the emperor himself, but before the prefect of the city, who had taken over the work of some of the other magistrates. No advocate would plead my cause; no one dared to appear as witness for me.

My trial was held in one of the great basilicas of the Forum, with a multitude of curious and hateful spectators looking on. The prefect and his assessors sat on a platform at one end of the great rectangular structure, which had its central portion open to the sky. The trial was hurried and unfair.

I was dragged before the court, accused not only on my former charge of treason, but this time also of having plotted to burn the city.

I defended myself as best I could, and preached the Word of God to the prefect and all the vast assemblage. I was not immediately condemned, but remanded to prison to await the second stage of my trial.

And here I have remained some months, writing this record of my life, though with difficulty, as I am under heavy guard and in confined quarters.

Luke has been with me, and at times also Tychicus, and Onesiphorus, and Linus; also Pudens, and Claudia his bride. I have longed for Timothy, and have but recently written to him * urging him to come. The time draws short.

*   *   *

Yesterday I was again taken to the basilica; my case was judged; I was condemned. Because I am a Roman, I am to die not meanly, on a cross or in the flames, as many others have done, but by the sword.

At any moment now, I shall be taken to a point outside the walls for execution. The guard will come, and I shall march between two files of Roman soldiers to some appointed roadside spot, where the deed will be accomplished.

My work is done. I have fought a good fight, I have finished my course, I have kept the faith. Henceforth there is laid up for me a crown of righteousness, which the Lord, the righteous judge, shall give me at that day: and not to me only, but to all them also that love his appearing.

*   *   *

The guard has come.

O death, where is thy sting? O grave, where is thy victory?

* The Second Epistle to Timothy.

MR, 14

1st Ed

name on half-title

stain 1st 6 pp

✓ Jacket Tears

✓ 5.00